MATH
IN
100
NUMBERS

METRO BOOKS
New York

An Imprint of Sterling Publishing Co., Inc.
1166 Avenue of the Americas
New York, NY 10036

ISBN: 978-1-4351-5800-9

For information about custom editions, special sales, and
premium and corporate purchases, please contact
Sterling Special Sales at 800-805-5489
or specialsales@sterlingpublishing.com.

Manufactured in China

2 4 6 8 10 9 7 5 3 1

www.sterlingpublishing.com

Design and illustration by Simon Daley

Conceived, designed, and produced by
Quid Publishing
Part of The Quarto Group
Level 4 Sheridan House
114 Western Road
Hove BN3 1DD
England

www.quidpublishing.com

MATH

IN

100

NUMBERS

A Numerical Guide to Facts,
Formulas, and Theories

COLIN STUART

METRO BOOKS
New York

Table of contents

Introduction

Math divides people. Attitudes toward the subject are probably more polarized than any other we study at school. Many are quick to identify themselves as "no good with numbers" or "not a math person." Yet math is merely a language, just like any other. Often it is even written in letters, just like spoken languages.

Learning math, again as with any new language, takes a little patience, but the rewards are huge. That's because math is Nature's language of choice. Our universe is inherently mathematical. Having a basic math vocabulary equips you with an incredibly powerful toolkit for grappling with the increasingly complex world around us. As we'll see, humans started playing around with numbers tens of thousands of years ago. And as time has gone by we've chipped away at the mathematical coal face, mining many of the secrets it has to offer. Early on we carved prime numbers into animal bones and clay tablets and used our knowledge of triangles and geometry to build towering pyramids and other ancient wonders. Today we manipulate strings of zeroes and ones to power the modern high-tech age.

But by no means is the story of our journey complete. Only recently, with the advent of powerful computing, have we solved mathematical mysteries that have stood for centuries. Some still remain unsolved—with huge financial incentives on offer to find the key to understanding them. Yet math isn't all about cold hard calculation, it can be fun too. Throughout these pages I have scattered details of recreational math puzzles—quirky features of numbers that have no inherent benefit other than they show how beautiful math can be. After all, it is the "Queen of the Sciences."

A note on symbols

Math is a subject full of symbols, with some of them very familiar to us. Take, for example, the +, −, ÷, and × symbols for the basic mathematical tasks of addition, subtraction, division, and multiplication.

Throughout these pages there will, however, be some symbols which are likely to be less familiar to you. Each will be explained when it appears, but here's a quick guide to get you started.

Symbol	Name	Meaning
$\sqrt{}$	Square root	To raise to the power of $\frac{1}{2}$
$\sum$	Sigma	To sum up a series of terms
$\int$	Integral	To perform the process of integration
!	Factorial	To multiply the number preceding the ! by every low number between it and 1
$\neq$	Inequality	"Does not equal to"

0

The additive identity

For a long time, humans were content to have a number list without a zero, or O. After all, the reason we invented numbers in the first place was to count and, in particular, to trade. Having a sense of size is particularly useful in these scenarios—I will swap you 2 goats for 1 pig. Under these circumstances, the numbers 1 and 2 make sense. Swapping O pigs for O goats doesn't have the same appeal.

The first time zero started to creep into our number lists was when it was used as a place holder. We'll see later that the number system widely used around the world today—the Hindu-Arabic numeral system—is a particularly efficient one (see page 92). We can denote a number that is ten times bigger than another simply by placing a zero at the end: 1 becomes 10, which becomes 100, etc. However, used in this way, zero isn't a number in and of itself—it's just a tool.

▲ Indian mathematician Brahmagupta was the first to consider the implications of zero as a number in its own right in 628 CE.

Not just for counting

It was only from the seventh century onward that zero came to be considered a number in its own right. In his 628 CE book *Brahmasputha Siddhanta* ("The Opening of the Universe"), the Indian mathematician and astronomer Brahmagupta was the first to lay out the rules of zero. If you add or subtract zero from a number, that number doesn't change—it maintains its identity. So modern mathematicians refer to zero as the additive identity. Multiplying something by zero gives you zero—two batches of nothing is still nothing.

Yet the question of dividing by zero is more difficult, and Brahmagupta's answer on the matter was wrong. Let's look at what happens to the value of $1/x$ as we make the value of x smaller and smaller:

Value of x	Value of $1/x$
2	0.5
1	1
0.5	2
0.25	4
0.1	10
0.01	100
0.001	1000

You can see that the closer x gets to 0, the higher and higher the value of $1/x$ becomes. So you might assume that $1/0 = \infty$ (the symbol for "infinity"). Yet this is wrong for several reasons. First, infinity isn't actually a number at all but a concept (see page 168). Second, if you tried the same thing with $2/x$, you would get the same conclusion—that it, too, was equal to infinity. If $1/0$ and $2/0$ are both equal to the same thing, then that leads to the crazy idea that $1 = 2$, something that Brahmagupta failed to address.

Finally, you only get the answer of ∞ if you start with values of x that are positive. If you redraw the same table but replace each number in the first column with its negative equivalent, then you would infer that the answer was $-\infty$.

So, actually, anything divided by zero is what mathematicians refer to as "undefined." Try to do it on a calculator and it will simply return the answer "error."

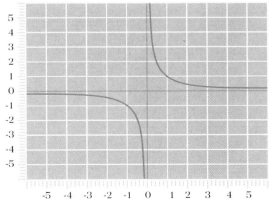

▼ Looking at what happens to $1/x$ and $-1/x$ for small values of x reveals the problem of dividing by zero.

1

The multiplicative identity

It is one of the most familiar numbers to us, but mathematicians have more than one way to refer to the number 1. It is known as the "multiplicative identity," because any number multiplied by 1 doesn't change—it keeps its own identity. This is similar to zero, which is called the additive identity (see page 10). You might also hear a mathematician refer to 1 as "unity."

It is the first "natural" number, too, meaning it begins the list of counting numbers. However, it isn't sufficient to have natural numbers alone. What if you wanted to divide 10 into 3 parts? There is no natural number to describe this. Nor is there a natural number to express 5 less than 2. So mathematicians also classify numbers in many other ways (see the box opposite).

In a practical sense, one of its most useful roles is in standardizing data sets. Say you want to compare the data in set 1, where the numbers range from 12 to 121, to those in set 2, where its numbers range from 3 to 83. Because the numbers within the two data sets are spread over different ranges, it can be difficult to compare them like for like. However, by using a process called "normalization," you can compare them more easily. Normalization converts every number in each set into a number between 0 and 1 via the following formula:

$$\frac{x - A}{B - A}$$

where x is the number within the set you want to normalize and A and B are the highest and lowest numbers in the set.

Number types

Natural numbers ($\mathbb{N}$) These are the standard counting numbers: 1, 2, 3, 4, ...

Whole numbers The natural numbers with the addition of zero: 0, 1, 2, 3, ...

Integers ($\mathbb{Z}$) All the natural numbers with their negative counterparts: ..., -2, -1, 0, 1, 2, ...

Rational numbers ($\mathbb{Q}$) Any number that can be expressed as the ratio of two non-zero integers, e.g. 0.75 = ¾.

Irrational numbers Any number that cannot be expressed as the ratio of two non-zero integers, e.g. π (see page 30).

Transcendental numbers Any number where the digits after the decimal point continue forever without a recurring pattern, e.g. e (see page 22).

Real numbers ($\mathbb{R}$) As distinct from imaginary numbers (see below). The group of real numbers contains all the integers, rational numbers, irrational numbers, and transcendental numbers.

Imaginary numbers A number comprising the number i, which is the $\sqrt{-1}$ (see page 102). Zero is considered both real and imaginary.

Complex numbers ($\mathbb{C}$) A number that has both a real and an imaginary part, e.g. 3 + 2i (see page 103)

So if set 1 contained the number 73, it would be normalized to:

$$\frac{73 - 12}{121 - 12} = \frac{61}{109} = 0.56$$

Similarly, if set 2 contained the number 59, it would be normalized to:

$$\frac{59 - 3}{83 - 3} = \frac{56}{80} = 0.7$$

Now you can easily see that even though 59 is lower than 73, it appears higher up in set 2 than 73 does in set 1.

1.306...

Mills' constant

As we'll see, prime numbers are the bedrock of mathematics (see page 20), so mathematicians are always interested in ways of finding them. In 1947, mathematician William H. Mills hit upon a way of generating prime numbers with the following formula:

$$\lfloor A^{3^n} \rfloor$$

(the corners around the equation—known as "floor brackets"— mean that you must round your answer down to the nearest whole number). Mills was able to find a value for A, which means that if you start replacing n with 1 and then 2 and then 3 and so on, it churns out prime numbers. That value for A is 1.306 (to three decimal places) and is known as Mills' constant.

Let's try it. When n = 1, we just end up with 1.306^3 ("cubed"), which on a calculator comes out as 2.229. Rounded down that gives us 2, the first prime number. For n = 2, we have 1.3063^{3^2}, which is the same as 1.3063^9 and equals 11.076. Lo and behold, 11 is a prime number. So this method doesn't give you all the primes (it skipped 3, 5, and 7), but it is a useful way of generating them.

However, this is only true if something called the Riemann hypothesis is also true. The hypothesis, named after German mathematician Bernhard Riemann, is a guess as to how prime numbers are ordered. And yet mathematicians are not certain it is true. So desperate are they for proof that there is a $1,000,000 prize on offer for anyone who can prove it (see page 153).

$\sqrt{2}$ (1.414...)

Pythagoras's constant

If we walk away from our math lessons with only one concept ingrained in our heads, it is probably the Pythagorean theorem. That is, the square of the length of the longest side of a right triangle is equal to the sum of the squares of the lengths on the other two sides. In short, $c^2 = a^2 + b^2$.

Imagine a right triangle (one with a 90° angle) with its two shortest sides each with a length of 1. According to the Pythagorean theorem, the square of the longest side—called the hypotenuse—is equal to $1^2 + 1^2 = 2$. The length of the hypotenuse, therefore, is the square root of that answer. This number is known as Pythagoras's constant and is 1.41 to two decimal places. It is an example of an irrational number—the decimal places never end or repeat. This means irrational numbers cannot be neatly written down as fractions.

An ancient idea

Pythagoras (ca. 569 BCE–ca. 500 BCE) may be one of the most famous mathematicians in history (see box on page 17), but he certainly wasn't the first to notice this idea. It wasn't even widely known as his theorem until the fourth century CE. Ancient Babylonian clay tablets from at least a millennium before

▼ The Plimpton 322 clay tablet from ancient Babylonia shows that people had an appreciation of the Pythagorean theorem as early as 1800 BCE.

Pythagoras show rules for calculating the length of the hypotenuse, as well as an approximation of $\sqrt{2}$ (said "root 2") to several decimal places.

The constant bears Pythagoras's name because he was probably the first to prove that the relationship holds for all such triangles. His exact method is shrouded in mystery, because he refused to write down any of his work. However, it is probable that he used geometry—the branch of mathematics that deals with shapes.

Take a right triangle that has its two shortest sides equal to 3 and 4 respectively. If the Pythagorean theorem is true, the length of the hypotenuse should be 5 as $5^2 = 3^2 + 4^2$. To check this, we can use the two shortest sides of the triangle to draw two squares. The first square will have an area of 9 (3 × 3) and the second square an area of 16 (4 × 4). If we also draw a square on the hypotenuse, we can see that its area is equal to 25, or 16 + 9.

Numbers such as 3, 4, 5 that satisfy Pythagoras's theorem are known as Pythagorean triples and are useful in construction. For example, we know the Ancient Egyptians used ropes with 12 knots equally spaced along them. By forming the rope into a triangle, so that there were 3 knots on one side, 4 on another, and five on the longest side, they could accurately mark out perfect right triangles.

$a^2 + b^2 = c^2$

c

b

a

b^2

a^2

◀ Although his exact method is unclear, Pythagoras potentially proved the theorem that bears his name by drawing squares on each side of a right triangle.

Pythagoras (ca. 569 BCE–ca. 500 BCE)

Born on the Greek Island of Samos, Pythagoras was far from the rational stereotype we have of mathematicians and scientists today. A mystic who founded his own religion—Pythagoreanism—legend has it that when he finally proved the theorem that bears his name he ritualistically sacrificed 100 oxen. His followers were also scared of beans—they were believed to contain the souls of the dead.

Pythagoreans were obsessed with the beauty in numbers, particularly whole numbers. Carved in stone above their school were the words "All is number." So when Pythagoras realized that $\sqrt{2}$ is irrational—that it cannot be expressed as a ratio of his cherished whole numbers—it reportedly sent him into a tailspin. He is said to have labeled these numbers "unutterable." Some historians believe that when Pythagorean philosopher Hippasus tried to tell the world of these irrational numbers, he conveniently drowned at sea.

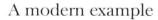

A modern example

These ideas are powerful in modern times, too. For example, around 1980, American electrical engineer Robert Metcalfe formulated what is now known as Metcalfe's law. It states that the value of a network—such as a telecommunications network—is related to the square of the number of users. While the validity of this idea is still the subject of debate, Pythagoras's ideas provide an interesting insight.

Imagine one network with five users, another with four, and another with three. As $5^2 = 4^2 + 3^2$, the Pythagorean theorem combined with Metcalfe's law implies that the single network with five users is more powerful than the two separate networks combined, even though they have a total of seven users. This idea has been used to approximate the way that the power of social networks, such as Facebook and Twitter, grows as their number of users increases.

φ (1.618...)

The golden ratio

In the thirteenth century, Leonardo of Pisa—known as Fibonacci (see box, opposite)—published a book containing a now famous list of numbers: 0, 1, 1, 2, 3, 5, 8, 13, 21, 34, 55, ... This is the Fibonacci sequence, with subsequent terms created by adding together the previous two terms. Something interesting happens when you divide each number by the one before it (their "ratio"). The more terms you add, the closer and closer the ratio gets to a number beginning 1.618. This was proved centuries later by German astronomer and mathematician Johannes Kepler (see page 74). Known as the "golden ratio," and given the symbol φ (said "fie"), its exact value is equal to $(1 + \sqrt{5})/2$.

However, the idea of a golden ratio stretches back even farther—the first recorded definition appears in 308 BCE in Euclid's famous mathematical publication *Elements* (see page 37). It is often stated that the ancient Greeks were obsessed with the golden ratio and even constructed great buildings, such as the Parthenon, using it. It seems, however, this idea has become overblown, the result of modern thinkers trying to retrospectively ascribe unwarranted significance. The same is the case for the idea that da Vinci's Vitruvian man was drawn using the golden ratio. In fact, there is a bit of a cult for erroneously ascribing significance to φ.

▼ A Fibonacci spiral. This shapes gets approximately φ times farther away from the center after each successive quarter turn.

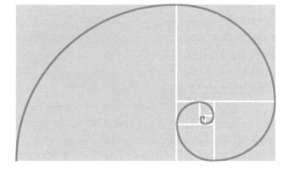

Fibonacci (ca. 1170–ca. 1250)

Born in Pisa, Italy, Fibonacci published the 1202 book *Liber Abaci* ("Book of Calculation"), which not only contained the Fibonacci sequence but was also responsible for bringing the Hindu-Arabic numeral system to Europe (see page 92). Fibonacci had encountered it during his travels to Algeria as a young boy with his father.

He originally came up with his famous numbers while thinking about the breeding habits of rabbits, although it wasn't until the nineteenth century that they became known as the Fibonacci sequence.

Not in the nautilus

It is often said that φ appears in nature, particularly in the shell of a species of mollusk known as the nautilus. To see why, we need to look at a Fibonacci rectangle. It is constructed by joining together squares with lengths equal to the terms in the Fibonacci sequence, then drawing one-quarter of a circle inside each square. Due to the way it's constructed, each point on the spiral is approximately 1.618 times farther from the center after each quarter turn. It is only approximate because the ratio of terms in the Fibonacci sequence gets close to φ only after a number of terms.

A spiral constructed so that it gets a fixed number of times farther away each time is known as a "logarithmic" spiral. If that fixed number is exactly φ, then it is called a "golden" spiral. The shells of creatures such as the nautilus mollusk do indeed have a logarithmic spiral shape; however, the fixed number by which their spiral gets farther away from the center is not φ. It does, however, appear many times in mathematics, including in the dimensions of the Platonic solids (see page 36).

▲ A nautilus shell. While its shape is a logarithmic spiral, the ratio of each successive twist is not equal to the golden ratio.

2

Lowest prime number

The prime numbers are to mathematicians what bricks are to builders. Everything in math is constructed out of them.

A prime is any number that can be divided by exactly two other numbers: 1 and itself. So 1 isn't prime because it can only be divided by one number (itself). Zero isn't prime either, because zero can be divided by every number except itself (see page 10). That makes 2 the lowest prime, and, incidentally, also the only even prime because all other even numbers can be divided by 2.

Any number that isn't prime is referred to as "composite," because it can be built out of prime "bricks" multiplied together. For example, 6 = 2 × 3 or 99 = 3 × 3 × 11. These bricks are known as "prime factors." We'll see in later chapters that mathematicians have come up with many ways to find prime numbers and to test whether a number is prime or composite.

Infinitely many primes

But just how many prime numbers are there? Well, as long ago as 300 BCE, in his work *Elements* (see page 37),

Quick ways for checking if a number is prime

If the sum of a number's digits is divisible by 3, then that number is also divisible by 3 and hence not prime. For example, to test 351, 3+5+1 = 9 which is divisible by 3 and so 351 is not prime.

With the exception of 5, any number ending in 5 is not prime because it will be divisible by 5. Likewise, any number ending in 0 is divisible by 10.

Euclid was able to show there are infinitely many—the list never ends. We can prove it, too, by showing that the opposite is false, known by mathematicians as a "proof by contradiction."

Let's assume the number of primes is finite. That means we should be able to write them all down in a list. Let's represent the first prime number as p_1, the second as p_2, the third as p_3, and so on, all the way up to the last prime number, which we'll call p_n.

Next, we introduce a number we'll call Q, which we find by multiplying every prime number in the list together and then adding 1.

Now, Q itself is either going to be prime or composite—there are no other options. If it is prime, well, it doesn't appear on our original list and so our list cannot be complete. If it is composite, then we must be able to write it as a multiplication of its prime factors, just

1	2	3	4	5	6	7	8	9	10
11	12	13	14	15	16	17	18	19	20
21	22	23	24	25	26	27	28	29	30
31	32	33	34	35	36	37	38	39	40
41	42	43	44	45	46	47	48	49	50
51	52	53	54	55	56	57	58	59	60
61	62	63	64	65	66	67	68	69	70
71	72	73	74	75	76	77	78	79	80
81	82	83	84	85	86	87	88	89	90
91	92	93	94	95	96	97	98	99	100

like we did with 6 and 99 on the page opposite. However, it is already equal to all the prime numbers in existence plus 1, so we'd need more prime numbers in order to do so. The only conclusion is that there must be other primes not on our list, so that list cannot be complete—there are infinitely many prime numbers.

▲ The prime numbers below 100. Notice how they are unevenly distributed: discovering a pattern in the primes is the holy grail of mathematics.

e (2.718...)
Euler's number

This number is one of the most ubiquitous and famous in math. It takes its name from Swiss mathematician Leonhard Euler (see box, opposite). However, it wasn't actually discovered by him. That honor goes to Euler's fellow countryman Jacob Bernoulli, but it was Euler who first denoted it by the letter e.

Bernoulli's discovery came while looking at money and interest. There are two main types of interest: simple and compound. Simple interest is only paid on the money you initially invest, whereas compound interest also applies to any interest previously accrued.

So if you invest $1 with a simple annual interest rate of 100%, at the end of the first year your money will have grown to $2. If it was in a compound interest account instead, with interest paid every six months, you would finish the year with $2.25. This is because the initial interest you received after six months ($0.50) itself earned interest in the second six months. The more often interest is paid, the more chance it has to work for you. Paid weekly, you would end up with $2.69 and daily would give you $2.71. The more frequently interest is paid, the closer and closer the result gets to e.

▼ Jacob Bernoulli discovered a link between the amount of compound interest paid on an investment and the number now known as e.

Leonhard Euler (1707–1783)

"Read Euler, read Euler, he is the master of us all." That was the view of French mathematician Pierre-Simon Laplace (1749–1827). Indeed, Euler is regarded by many as the greatest mathematician of the eighteenth century and appears many times in the pages that follow.

He was born in the northern Swiss city of Basel to a religous family (his father was a pastor). He attended the local university at the age of just 13 and quickly showed mathematical promise. By 1727, he had moved to Russia to join his friend Daniel Bernoulli (son of Jacob) who was at the Academy at St. Petersburg, which had recently been founded by Peter the Great.

He is widely credited with bringing many modern conventions to mathematics, including the use of functions and denoting them as $f(x)$, i for the imaginary unit (see page 102), Σ for summing a series (see page 158), and, of course, e for the number that now bears his name.

It is the basis of natural logarithms, too (see page 104), and was first alluded to in a logarithmic table published in a book by John Napier in 1618, making that an earlier use than Bernoulli's. However, the book didn't explicitly mention the constant or give it a name. It can also be found as part of the exponential function e^x, hence why Euler gave it the letter e. Exponential functions are used to describe processes that involve continuous growth or decay (for example, compound interest or radioactive decay).

Its place among the pantheon of major mathematical constants is cemented by its appearance alongside the imaginary unit (see page 102), π (see page 30), 1, and zero in "Euler's identity," which says that $e^{i\pi}-1 = 0$.

3

Main types of triangles

As its name suggests, a triangle is any two-dimensional shape (polygon) that has three internal angles. However, triangles are more often classified into three groups based on the relative lengths of their three sides (see below and right). When drawing these triangles, short marks are used to show which sides are the same length and arcs are used to show which angles match.

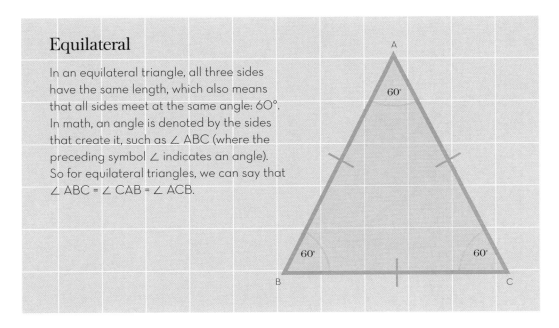

Equilateral

In an equilateral triangle, all three sides have the same length, which also means that all sides meet at the same angle: 60°. In math, an angle is denoted by the sides that create it, such as ∠ ABC (where the preceding symbol ∠ indicates an angle). So for equilateral triangles, we can say that ∠ ABC = ∠ CAB = ∠ ACB.

Isosceles

Here, only two of the three sides are of equal length. The two internal angles that lie opposite the equal lengths are also themselves equal. This fact is known as *pons asinorum*, which is Latin for "bridge of donkeys" and appears in Euclid's *Elements* (see page 37). It is thought to get its name from the fact that if a student could not prove the statement of *pons asinorum* to be true, they would probably not be able to move on to higher math.

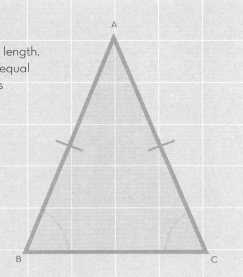

Scalene

This is a triangle with no equal sides and, therefore, no equal internal angles. Unlike equilateral and isosceles triangles, scalene triangles have one, two, and three short lines and one, two, and three arcs to make it clear that all lengths and angles differ. So in this case, ∠ ABC ≠ ∠ CAB ≠ ∠ ACB (where ≠ is the mathematical symbol for "does not equal").

3
Lowest Mersenne prime

A Mersenne prime is a prime number that is also 1 less than a power of 2. In formal notation this is written as $M_n = 2^n - 1$.

Take 2^5 (said "2 to the power 5"), which is $2 \times 2 \times 2 \times 2 \times 2 = 32$. One less than 32 is 31, which is a prime number. That makes 31 a Mersenne prime (known as M_5). The lowest such prime (M_2) is 3, because $2^2 - 1 = 3$. The first four (3, 7, 31, and 127) were all found by ancient Greek mathematicians. The tenth in the list, $2^{89} - 1$, wasn't found until the twentieth century.

Not always right

They are named after French friar Marin Mersenne (1588–1648), who is said to have come up with 11. However, he got two wrong and skipped three on his list. Mersenne had claimed that $2^{67} - 1$ was prime, yet in 1903 American mathematician Frank Cole showed that it was not. Cole stood silently in front of a meeting of the American Mathematical Society and calculated $2^{67} - 1$ as 147,573,952,589,676,412,927 on a blackboard. He then wrote 193,707,721 × 761,838,257,287 on the other side of the board and did the multiplication to show the answer, in fact, matched the first number he'd calculated. He returned to his seat without saying a word. It had taken him "three years of Sundays" to find the factors of the supposed M_{67}.

3

Number of elementary trigonometric functions

The Pythagorean theorem may tell us about the lengths of the sides of a right triangle (see page 15), but to calculate a length you must already know the other two. What if you only know one of the lengths? Well, as long as you also know one of the two nonright angles you can still work out a missing length. Similarly, if you know the lengths of two of the sides, you can work out an angle. These calculations form part of an area of mathematics known as trigonometry. Trigonometry can also be used to work

Joseph Fourier (1768–1830)

The son of a tailor, Fourier was born in Auxerre, France, and was an orphan by the age of nine. Despite the low standing of his birth, he eventually worked his way up through societal ranks and was appointed scientific advisor to Napoleon on his expedition to Egypt in 1798.

His most notable scientific achievement came when he turned his attention to the puzzle of how heat propagates through solid bodies. He was able to solve an equation for heat transfer by modeling the heat source as a series of sine and cosine waves. The combination of these waves is known as a Fourier Series.

out angles in triangles that do not contain a right angle, although those rules are more complicated.

Trigonometric triangles

In order to perform these calculations, mathematicians use three trigonometric functions whose full names are sine, cosine, and tangent (they are often abbreviated to just sin, cos, and tan). The three sides of the right triangle are also given names (see diagram, below). As before, the longest side is always called the hypotenuse. The other two sides are labeled as opposite and adjacent, based on their relationship to the angle you know (or want to find out). The angle itself is conventionally denoted by the Greek letter θ ("theta").

There are three trigonometric rules that let you calculate missing angles or lengths. The same two sides always pair up with the same trigonometric function: sin goes with opposite and hypotenuse; cos goes with adjacent and hypotenuse; and tan goes with opposite and adjacent. This is sometimes written out as SOH CAH TOA to help remember it. Alternatively, people often use mnemonics, such as **S**ome **O**ld **H**ag **C**racked **A**ll **H**er **T**eeth **O**n **A**pples. The three rules are, then, as follows:

sin θ = opposite/hypotenuse
cos θ = adjacent/hypotenuse
tan θ = opposite/adjacent

Their power is perhaps best seen with an example. Take the triangle shown here. If you want to calculate the length of the opposite side, you would use the sin function (because sin goes with opposite and the hypotenuse we already have). We can say that:

sin 30° = opposite/5

Using a calculator, sin 30° = 0.5. We also know that the opposite side must be 5 times bigger than this, so its length must be 2.5—exactly half the length of the hypotenuse. Alternatively, we can work backward to find the angle. Let's say we already knew

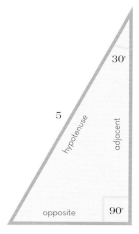

▲ If you know one of the two nonright angles and the length of a side, you can use trigonometry to calculate the length of another side.

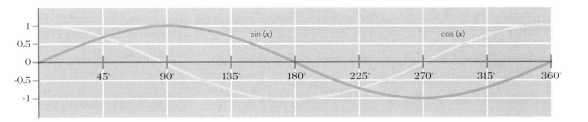

the hypotenuse was 5 and the opposite side was 2.5. Then we could write:

$$\sin \theta = 2.5/5 = 0.5$$

To calculate the angle here, you use the "inverse sin function" denoted on a calculator as sin⁻¹. So:

$$\sin^{-1}(0.5) = 30°$$

Not just triangles

The three elementary trigonometric functions have uses far beyond triangles and geometry. If you plot a graph of the values that sin θ and cos θ take as you vary the angle between 0° and 360°, you end up with what looks like a wave (as shown in the diagram above). For values above 360°, the pattern simply repeats itself. For this reason, both sine and cosine are known as "periodic" functions (the tangent function is slightly different but is still periodic).

The repeating wavelike nature of the sine function is particularly useful in physics and engineering for modeling the behavior of things that act like waves, such as light and sound. The electricity supplied to your house is in the form of alternating current (AC) and if you plot the voltage over time it looks like a sine wave—it is said to show sinusoidal variation. A lot of physics and engineering also relies on being able to reduce more complex periodic functions to a series of simpler sine and cosine waves all added together. Breaking the complex function into its more basic constituents is known as Fourier analysis, named after the French mathematician Joseph Fourier (see box on page 27).

π (3.141...)
Pi

Along with the Pythagorean theorem (see page 15), the symbol π (said "pie") is synonymous with high school math. It is the ratio of the distance around a circle (its "circumference") to the distance across it (its "diameter"). So, if a circle has a diameter of 1 inch, it will have a circumference approximately equal to 3.14 inches. I say "approximately," because π is an irrational number—the numbers after the decimal point go on forever, never repeating in any pattern. Said another way, you can't write it neatly as a fraction.

This ratio wasn't represented by the π symbol until the mid-eighteenth century, but it has been known since at least the eighteenth century BCE. A Babylonian tablet excavated in 1936 and dating from around this time contains mathematical text clearly showing an approximation of π as 25/8 (equal to 3.125). That's only a 0.5% discrepancy from the real value. By the fourth century BCE, astronomers were using 339/108—just 0.09% out.

Book of π

The record for the most number of decimal places calculated without a computer was set by Englishman William

Areas and volumes with π

π can be used to calculate the areas and volumes of any shape based on the circle. In the following formulae, r = radius (half the diameter) and h = height.

Area of circle = πr^2
Volume of a sphere = $4/3\ \pi r^3$
Surface area of a sphere = $4\pi r^2$
Volume of a cylinder = $\pi r^2 h$
Volume of a cone = $1/3\ \pi r^2 h$

Buffon's needle

In the eighteenth century, Georges-Louis Leclerc, Comte de Buffon, posed a question that at first seems to have little to do with π. However, the solution gives an illustration of just how ubiquitous it is, even beyond circles, areas, and volumes.

Buffon imagined a floor made of parallel strips of wood onto which you drop a series of needles of an equal size, each smaller than the width of the wooden strips. What is the probability of a needle landing in such a way that it lies across the line between two adjoining strips?

The formula relating x (the number of needles lying across a boundary) to n (the total number of needles dropped) is:

$$x \approx \frac{2nl}{\pi t}$$

where l is the length of the needles and t is the width of the wooden strips.

So, if you were so inclined, you could do the experiment for yourself and find an approximation for π by rearranging to equation to:

$$\pi \approx \frac{2nl}{xt}$$

and dropping a few dozen needles (the more the better).

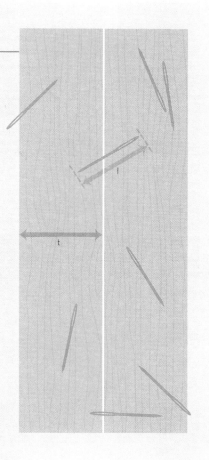

Shanks, who was able to successfully work out 527 digits by hand in 1873. By 1989, computers had extended our knowledge to more than a billion digits for the first time. Today, we know it to a staggering 12.1 trillion digits. In Times New Roman font size 10 a letter-size page contains just under 5,500 characters, so you would need 1.1 billion pages (front and back) to write out all the digits. With each page 0.05 millimeters thick—that's ¹/₅₈₀ of an inch—your "book of π" would itself be 34 miles thick.

4

Basic types of shape transformation

In math, manipulating shapes in such a way that their appearance changes is called a transformation, and there are four main ways it can be done: translation, rotation, reflection, and resizing. The original shape is called the "object" and the new shape called the "image." If translation, rotation, or reflection are used, the object and image are referred to as "congruent." If the object is resized, then both it and the image are "similar."

Translation

A translation involves moving an object up or down or side to side but without changing its orientation. Every corner of the shape (vertex) must be moved by the same amount. The amount to move the shape is called a "displacement vector" and is written as two numbers, one above the other, inside a set of parentheses, for example $\left(\begin{smallmatrix}-2\\3\end{smallmatrix}\right)$. The top number tells you how many units to move the shape right (positive numbers) or left (negative numbers). The bottom number says how many units to move the shape up (positive numbers) or down (negative numbers).

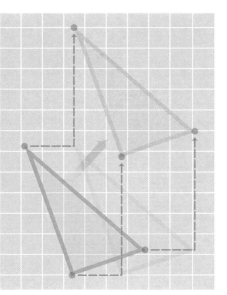

Rotation

All rotations must take place around a fixed center of rotation. The amount of turning must also be specified. This can be done in terms of degrees or in terms of a fraction of one complete turn (¼, ½, ¾, etc). Any point in the original object and its corresponding point in the image must always be the same distance from the center of rotation.

Reflection

As its name suggests, reflections are the equivalent of redrawing an object as if it were seen in a mirror. The position over which the shape is reflected—the effective position of the imaginary mirror—is called the "mirror line." The object and the image are always the same perpendicular (right angle) distance from the mirror line.

Resizing

When changing the size of a shape, it is important to know not just how much to increase or decrease its size (known as the "scale factor") but also from which point to begin the resizing ("center of enlargement"). This can be located either inside or outside of the original shape, which will result in different images.

4

Number of colors in
a famous theorem

Imagine a map of the world. How many colors would you need to fill it in so that no two adjoining countries share the same color? It turns out the answer is four, but proving this Four Color Theorem turned out to be notoriously tricky.

The question was first formally posed in 1852 by South African mathematician Francis Guthrie. He was attempting to color in the counties of England and realized that it could always be done using a maximum of four colors—a fifth was never required. Francis's brother Frederick took the problem to the renowned British mathematician Augustus De Morgan, who searched in vain for a mathematical proof. He was the first in a long line of mathematicians who would become frustrated with this deceptively difficult problem. His successors toiled for more than a century, attempting different ways to prove it. Many times along the way apparent proofs were put forward, but all turned out to be wrong. In the end, it would take a computer to find the elusive proof, making the Four Color Theorem the first to be proved in such a way. On June 21, 1976, two colleagues at the University of Illinois, mathematicians Kenneth Appel and Wolfgang Haken, revealed their proof—they had used the computer to check 1,936 different configurations, which took more than 1,000 hours of computer processing time.

▼ It never takes more than four colors to complete any map in such a way that no adjoining regions share the same color.

δ (4.699...)

Feigenbaum's constant

A butterfly flaps its wings in the Amazon, causing it to rain in Tokyo. This famous idea is known as "the butterfly effect" and has its roots in math. In the 1960s, American meteorologist and mathematician Edward Lorenz was running computerized weather prediction models. On one run, his initial value for some variable was 0.506127. Trying to find a shortcut, he entered it as simply 0.506 on another run. And yet that seemingly small change led to a completely different outcome.

To explain his surprise that it made such a difference, Lorenz compared it to a seagull's wing flap affecting the weather. He would later switch his metaphorical creature to a butterfly.

Lorenz showed that certain systems are incredibly sensitive to even small changes in their initial conditions. The study of this field of mathematics is known as "chaos theory" and can trace its roots back to 1890, when Henri Poincaré (see page 153) noted a similar dependency for a certain type of system.

As a system becomes chaotic, you see an effect known as "period doubling," where the time it takes for a pattern of behavior to repeat becomes twice as long as before. Eventually, the behavior takes so long to repeat that the system appears chaotic, because there is an apparent lack of underlying order. In 1978, American mathematician Mitchell Feigenbaum worked out the ratio between the values of the points at which this doubling occurs and found that it always approached the same number: 4.699...

▼ "The butterfly effect" is used to symbolize a small change in one parameter causing a much bigger change in the overall system.

5

Number of Platonic solids

Tetrahedron

Cube

Octahedron

Shapes play a huge part in math, with different types of shapes having their own names. For example, flat shapes such as triangles, squares, and pentagons, are known as polygons (from the Greek for "many corners"). Similarly, solid three-dimensional shapes, such as the cube, are known as polyhedra (from the Greek for "many bases").

Of all the polyhedra you can construct, there are only five that can be made with faces that are all the same regular polygon. They are: the tetrahedron (made of 4 triangles), the cube (made of 6 squares), the octahedron (made of 8 triangles), the dodecahedron (made of 12 pentagons), and the icosahedron (made of 20 triangles). They are known as the Platonic solids, after the Greek philosopher Plato, although some historians suggest that Pythagoras was the one who discovered them.

To make a Platonic solid, three or more polygons must meet at a corner (or "vertex"). The internal angles of these polygons cannot add up to more than 360°, otherwise the shape would flatten out and it would no longer be a polyhedron. It turns out that only five combinations of shapes satisfy this requirement. Regular triangles have internal angles of 60°, which means you can have three, four, or even five triangles meeting at a vertex without exceeding 360°. Three squares (90° internal angles) and three pentagons (108° internal angles) are the only other shapes that work.

Dodecahedron

Icosahedron

Axioms in Euclid's *Elements*

The rules that surround two-dimensional shapes drawn on a flat plane (such as a sheet of paper) are known as Euclidean geometry, after the Greek mathematician Euclid, who wrote an early textbook on the subject called *Elements*.

Within its pages are five rules for what you can do with a pencil, ruler, and a pair of compasses.

1 You can always draw a straight line between two points.
2 There is no limit to how long a line can be.
3 Attaching a line to a point and moving it around will lead to a circle.
4 All right angles are equal to each other.
5 If you can draw a line across two other lines so that the two angles created adjacent to that line sum up to less than 180°, then the two original lines will intersect at some point (known as the Parallel Postulate, this is also a way of saying that the angles in a triangle add up to 180°).

Geometry that does not satisfy the Parallel Postulate is non-Euclidean geometry. Take, for example, a triangle drawn on the surface of the Earth. Start at the north pole and draw a line down to the equator. Take a 90° turn and travel along the equator for some distance before taking a 90° turn back up to the north pole. Those two angles add to 180°, so adding in the third angle must make the total over 180°.

▲ The ancient Greek mathematician Euclid is one of the most influential names in early mathematics. He is particularly famous for his work on geometry.

6

The smallest perfect number

Some numbers have special properties and are often singled out for this reason. Perfect numbers are those that are the sum of all the numbers that divide into them (except themselves). The smallest perfect number is 6, because 6 can be divided by 1, 2, and 3 and 1 + 2 + 3 = 6. Such numbers are few and far between. The next in the list is 28 (1 + 2 + 4 + 7 + 14 = 28), followed by 496 and 8,128. It is thought that as early as 100 CE Pythagorean mathematician Nicomachus had noted that 8,128 was "perfect." However, the fifth perfect number (33,550,336) wasn't identified until the sixteenth century.

In his famous work *Elements*, Euclid was able to prove a relationship between perfect numbers and Mersenne primes (see page 26). He demonstrated that if you take a Mersenne prime, add 1 to it, times it by itself, and then divide the answer by 2, you get an even perfect number. So take 3, the smallest Mersenne prime: 3(3+1)/2 = 6, the smallest perfect number. The next Mersenne prime is 7 and 7(7+1)/2 = 28, and the third Mersenne prime is 31 and 31(31+1)/2 = 496, etc. It remains to be proven whether there are any odd perfect numbers or whether there are infinitely many perfect numbers.

▲ As well as his work on perfect numbers, ancient Greek mathematician Nicomachus studied arithmetic and harmonics. He is believed to have followed the teachings of Pythagoras.

6.284... (2π)

Answer to the Rope Around the World puzzle

Like the Monty Hall problem (see page 68), the Rope Around the World puzzle is an example of how sometimes common sense can be deceptive. Imagine a rope that stretches all the way around the Earth along the equator, clinging to the planet's surface. By how much would you have to lengthen the rope in order to introduce a 1-foot gap between the ground and the rope?

When first confronted with the problem, you probably had a gut feeling that the rope would have to be extended by a long distance—after all, the Earth is a big planet. And yet the answer is a mere 6.284 feet (or 2π feet).

The circumference of the Earth (or any circle, for that matter) is $2 \times \pi \times$ the radius of the circle. So we can write the initial length of the rope as $2\pi r_{earth}$. If we are to raise the rope 1 foot above the ground, then the radius of the circle will also go up by 1 foot. So the circumference of the new rope is $2\pi(r_{earth} + 1)$. If we expand out the brackets we get $2\pi r_{earth} + 2\pi$. In other words, the length of the new rope is the length of the old rope plus 2π feet. Add just 6.284 feet to the rope and you can wrap it all the way around the Earth, hovering at a height of 1 foot above the equator.

▼ To raise a rope around the world by a set number of feet, extend the length of the rope by 2π multiplied by that number.

1 ft

Rope 24,901.55mi + 2π ft

Earth 24,901.55mi

7

Bridges in the
Königsberg problem

Math can sometimes seem like an abstract subject, far detached from the real world. In fact, it underpins almost every aspect of life. And by trying to solve real-world problems, mathematicians can sometimes make advances in their subject. One of the most famous examples of such a crossover concerns the seven bridges that spanned the Pregel River in the Prussian town of Königsberg during the eighteenth century. The city (now Kaliningrad in Russia) sits on both sides of the river and the water splits and rejoins in such a way as to create two islands between its banks.

By the 1700s, the locals, clearly with too much time on their hands, had set a challenge for themselves: to walk around the city by crossing each bridge exactly once. While that might seem a simple thing to do, no local could ever achieve it—it's impossible.

▼ A map showing the Prussian town of Königsberg with its seven bridges. It is impossible to walk around the town crossing all the bridges only once.

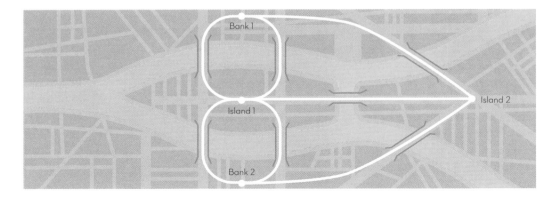

A new field emerges

The fact that their attempts were fruitless was eventually proven by Swiss mathematician Leonhard Euler (see page 23) in 1736 while in the service of Catherine the Great. In doing so, he created a new area of mathematics known as topology and a new type of diagram known as a network. A network shows how a series of objects are connected, with the objects themselves depicted using dots known as nodes (or vertices). The connections between them—called "edges"—are denoted by lines. These network diagrams are sometimes called graphs (not to be confused with the more familiar type of graph with an x and a y-axis), so their study is sometimes called graph theory.

In Euler's network, the four land areas (the two banks and the two islands) were drawn as nodes and the seven bridges that connected them all as edges. A network is considered "traversable" if you can place a pencil on a particular node and trace over each edge exactly once. By studying these networks, Euler was able to show they are only traversable under one of two conditions: if all nodes have an even number of edges meeting them, or if exactly two of the nodes have an odd number of edges meeting them. For the Königsberg network, all four nodes are met by an odd number of edges—the bridge network is not traversable.

When I was a youngster in school, one of the puzzles passed between pupils was to draw the shape of an envelope without ever lifting your pencil from the page. It turns out that this is possible because, of its six nodes, exactly two of them are met by an odd number of edges. There are only two possible ways, however, to solve the problem—you must begin drawing the shape at either odd node (and you will always end up at the other one).

Today, graph theory is used in a wide range of fields from genomics and electrical engineering to scheduling aircraft and delivery drivers, but it all started in Königsberg.

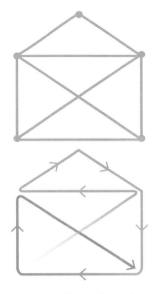

▲ A network in the shape of an envelope is traversable because exactly two of its nodes are met by an odd number of edges.

7

Fewest moves required to solve a three-disk Tower of Hanoi puzzle

The 2011 movie *Rise of the Planet of the Apes* saw the animals' intelligence tested using a pyramid game involving moving pieces around in a particular order. It is a version of a famous puzzle called the Tower of Hanoi, or Lucas' Tower after its inventor Édouard Lucas (see page 91).

In the simplest setup, there are three pegs and three round disks of different sizes. All three disks initially sit on the first peg in size order (largest at the bottom). The aim of the game is to re-create the same pile, but on the third peg. However, you can only move one disk at a time and you can never put a larger disk on top of a smaller one.

It's called the Tower of Hanoi because legend has it that at a monastery outside the Vietnamese city of Hanoi, there was a larger version of the game with 64 golden disks. The monks supposedly set about moving the disks according to the rules, and an ancient prophecy stated that the placing of the final piece would herald the end of the world. Some historians believe Lucas invented the legend for his own ends. Either way, completing the 64-disk puzzle would take an impossibly long time.

Mathematicians have shown that the minimum number of moves required to complete the puzzle is $2^n - 1$, where n is the number of disks. For the simple three-disk case, the number of moves required is only seven, whereas for 64 disks it would take 18,446,744,073,709,551,615 turns.

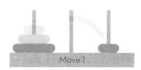

Move 1

Move 2

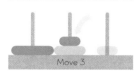

Move 3

Move 4

Move 5

Move 6

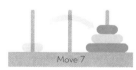

Move 7

▲ The moves required to solve the three-disk version of the puzzle. For any n disk puzzle, the number of moves required is $2^n - 1$.

10

The base system we use

Have you ever wondered why we celebrate someone turning 40 more than we do when they reach 39 or 41? It is because we have ten fingers on our hands. And it is no coincidence that they are also called digits.

In modern times, we use a base-10 system—that is, we count using only ten digits, 0–9 (in all likelihood to match our hands). To represent a number more than 9, we go back to 0 and add a 1 in front of it. So the number at the front of our age changes every ten years and we either party or console ourselves accordingly. If our hands had evolved with one fewer digit, we'd probably be counting in base-8 (known as an octal system) and you would be celebrating "significant" birthdays more frequently.

Humans haven't always used base-10. The Babylonians used base-60 (our use of 60 seconds in a minute and 60 minutes in an hour is a relic of this, see page 63). The Mayans used a base-20 system. Computers use binary, which only has two digits—0 and 1.

Decimal vs. binary vs. octal

The first ten decimal numbers and their equivalents in binary and octal.

Decimal (base-10)	Binary (base-2)	Octal (base-8)
1	1	01
2	10	02
3	11	03
4	100	04
5	101	05
6	110	06
7	111	07
8	1000	010
9	1001	011
10	1010	012

12.7

Frequency with which e appears in the English language (%)

The art of cryptography—encoding and decoding encrypted messages—is an ancient one. For millennia, everyone from lovers to generals have wanted to share their secrets without anyone else snooping on them.

In cryptography, the original message is known as "plaintext" and the encoded message as "ciphertext." To convert between one and the other, the sender and recipient must be in possession of the same set of encryption rules—the cipher. One of the simplest methods is known as the "Caesar cipher," after Roman emperor Julius Caesar. To encode a message in this way, replace each letter in the plaintext with another that is a set number of places away in the alphabet. So "fear the Ides of March" becomes "hgct vjg Kfgu qh Octej" if you shift every letter forward by two. If the person at the other end knows what you've done, they can turn the ciphertext back into the original message.

Too easy to solve

Of course, this is a relatively simple system to solve and it wouldn't take long for anyone intercepting your message to unscramble what you've done. A more complex method would be to replace the letters in a more random way. For example, you could use the following system:

A	B	C	D	E	F	G	H	I	J	K	L	M
J	Q	D	V	G	R	A	O	L	C	Z	H	S

N	O	P	Q	R	S	T	U	V	W	X	Y	Z
M	K	U	T	B	P	F	W	E	Y	N	I	X

As long as both sender and recipient were in possession of this agreed substitution, they could exchange messages—"fear the Ides of March" now becomes "rgjb fog lvgp kr Sjbdo." This is harder for a stranger to decipher than the original encryption; however, it is still a weak cipher, because it can be solved pretty easily using the mathematics of frequency analysis.

The idea is based on exploiting the frequency with which certain letters appear in the language the code is written in. For instance, in many European languages e is by far the most common letter. Its average frequency in English text is 12.7% (14.7% in French, 12.2% in Spanish, 16.4% in German, and 11.8% in Italian). Knowing this helps to solve the code, because whichever letter you've substituted for e in the ciphertext will appear with the same frequency. Find the letter that appears closest to 12.7% of the time and that will probably be e. The longer the text, the easier it is. The frequency of all letters in any language is well established and a computer is able to break the code with relative ease.

For this reason, no one uses substitution ciphers for serious encryption anymore. In circumstances where secrecy is of great importance—such as transmitting credit card details online—a form of encryption that utilizes prime numbers is used instead (see page 77).

Plaintext
Ciphertext

▲ Substituting one letter for another is one method for sending coded messages. Doing this randomly is harder to solve than a Caesar cipher.

13

Number of Archimedean solids

The Platonic solids (see page 36) are three-dimensional shapes constructed with faces made of identical polygons. By contrast, the Archimedean solids are three-dimensional shapes made from more than one type of polygon, with the condition that the arrangement around each polygon is identical. There are 13 in all, often with fantastic names, such as the rhombicuboctahedron (made from 8 triangles and 18 squares).

It is believed they were discovered by ancient Greek mathematician Archimedes, although records of his work haven't stood the test of time. Instead, the fourth-century Greek mathematician Pappus of Alexandria referred to Archimedes as the first person to come up with the list.

The Archimedean solids can actually be made by starting with the Platonic solids and performing certain operations on them. Truncation, for example, involves symmetrically cutting off corners (or "vertices"). If you cut the corners from a cube (Platonic solid), you end up with the truncated cube (Archimedean solid) made from 8 triangles and 6 octagons.

Archimedes (ca. 287 BCE–ca. 212 BCE)

Although perhaps best known for his "Eureka" moment in which he is said to have run naked down the street shouting after discovering the rules of buoyancy while in the bath, Archimedes was a true polymath. A mathematician, physicist, engineer, and astronomer, his other notable mathematical works include "Measurement of a Circle," in which he approximated π and noted that the area of a circle was equal to π times the square of the circle's radius.

Archimedean solids

The 13 Archimedean solids are found by starting with the 5 Platonic solids and altering them in a symmetrical way.

Cuboctahedron

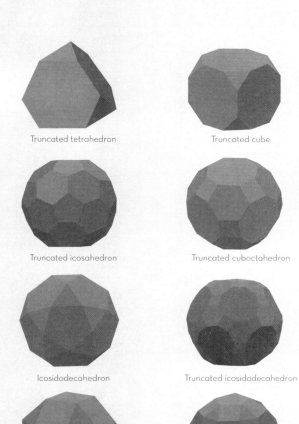

Truncated tetrahedron

Truncated cube

Truncated octahedron

Truncated icosahedron

Truncated cuboctahedron

Truncated dodecahedron

Icosidodecahedron

Truncated icosidodecahedron

Snub cube

Rhombicuboctahedron

Rhombicosidodecahedron

Snub dodecahedron

15

Number of racked balls at the start of a game of 8-ball pool

The 15 balls in the rack at the beginning of a game of 8-ball are arranged in a triangle. It is impossible, however, to start with say 11 or 12 balls and still have them arranged in that shape. To maintain the triangle you'd either have to remove the last row of 5 to make 10 or add another row of 6 to make 21. It is why in a game of 9-ball, the balls are instead arranged in a diamond formation.

By writing out the full list of possible balls in a triangular rack, we can create a list that mathematicians refer to as triangle numbers. The first few are 1, 3, 6, 10, 15, 21, 28, ...

You can see that the gap between each number in the series goes up by one more each time. Look at the rack of balls shown here: there is one in the first row, two in the second, three in the third, four in the fourth, and five in the fifth. To maintain a triangle, you would need six in the sixth.

You can use the formula n(n+1)/2 to work out any number in the list. If you wanted the tenth number, just put in 10 instead of n and you get 10(10+1)/2 = 55. You may have noticed that this formula is the same as that for calculating perfect numbers from Mersenne primes (see page 38). This means all perfect numbers are also triangle numbers.

▼ In pool, you can have a triangular rack only if the number of balls in it is equal to one of the triangle numbers.

16

Ounces in a pound

Many of history's greatest mathematicians, including Évariste Galois (see page 52), were wrapped up in the political turmoil that was revolutionary France. By 1792, the French monarchy had been abolished and the French Republic was founded. With the new political system came a new system of measurement too—the metric system. Based on powers of 10, it gave us measurements like the meter (100 centimeters) and the kilogram (1,000 grams). Almost every country in the world now officially uses this system. The only exceptions are the United States, Liberia, and Myanmar. However, in other countries, particularly the United Kingdom, the older Imperial system is still in widespread use (speed limits are in miles per hour, beer is sold in pints, and almost every British person gives their height in feet and inches).

The Imperial system is an ancient one, based largely on the human body or everyday items: the origins of the "foot" and "stone" need little explanation. Imperial units are often split up into 12 or 16 parts, such as 12 inches in a foot or 16 ounces in a pound. This was perhaps more practical than 10, which can be divided into only tenths, fifths, and halves—16 can be divided into sixteenths, eighths, quarters, and halves, all of which are double the size of the preceding division. However, the metric system is arguably more sensible for modern use, because it creates a standard system for everyone.

▼ The pound is a useful measurement because, being made up of 16 ounces, it can be split into smaller subdivisions more easily than 10.

17

Lowest Leyland prime number

A Leyland number, named after British software developer Paul Leyland, is any number that can be written as $x^y + y^x$. The only caveat is that x and y must both be bigger than 1. The first Leyland number is 8 ($2^2 + 2^2$). If you use 3 and 3 you end up with 54 ($3^3 + 3^3$), which is also the lowest number than can be written as the sum of three squares in three different ways:

$$54 = 7^2 + 2^2 + 1^2 = 6^2 + 3^2 + 3^2 = 5^2 + 5^2 + 2^2$$

Of particular interest are Leyland numbers that are also prime, the lowest being 17—it can be written $2^3 + 3^2$.

While there are many Leyland numbers, Leyland prime numbers are pretty rare. The next one after 17 is 593 and after that it is 32,993. The search for bigger and bigger Leyland primes continues. In December 2012, the largest confirmed Leyland prime was revealed to be $3,110^{63} + 63^{3110}$. It is possible that $314,738^9 + 9^{314738}$ is also prime, but proving that this number, with more than 300,000 digits, divides by no other numbers than 1 and itself is a fiendish task.

Paul Leyland has said that examining these large Leyland numbers helps to improve computer programs that are able to test for primality. This is important in areas such as Internet security, which depend on factoring large prime numbers (see page 77).

▼ Writing computer code that can search for Leyland numbers is good way to test the skills of students learning about programming.

18

Papers written by Karl Pearson that revolutionized statistics

The modern world is full of statistics, whether it is the latest political poll or the performances of your favorite sports team. And yet a rigorous treatment of stats is much younger than many other branches of mathematics. One man above all other is often singled out as the founder of modern statistical theory: Karl Pearson. Born in London in 1857, he began the statistical revolution at the beginning of the 1880s.

In 1893, he published the first of 18 papers on the subject under the title *Mathematical Contributions to the Theory of Evolution*, immediately showing how mathematics can be applied to other scientific disciplines.

Of his many contributions to statistics, perhaps his most famous invention is the p-value test—a way of determining the significance of a statistical result. Say you have a hunch that one variable changes the value of another. It could be, for example, that a college education increases your average salary. In practice, you cannot actually prove this to be true. Instead, you test to see if the opposite statement—known as the null hypothesis—can be shown to be false. If you perform Pearson's p-value test on a series of data you will get an answer between 0 and 1. The lower the number, the more probable it is that the null hypothesis can be rejected and you can be reasonably confident your suspected association is not due to chance.

▲ Karl Pearson (1857–1936) is considered by many to be the founding father of modern statistics. His 18 papers on the subject were revolutionary.

20

Age at which Évariste Galois died

Born in France in 1811, Évariste Galois made significant advances in mathematics, including solving a problem that had stood for more than three centuries. More remarkable, then, that he did so while still in his teens.

Much of his work centered around algebraic equations known as polynomials. A polynomic function is an equation that contains several terms added together or subtracted from one another. These terms can include powers (such as squared or cubed) but these "exponents" must be positive (that is, you can have x^2, but you cannot have x^{-2}).

A simple example of a polynomial function is $f(x) = x^2 + x - 2 = 0$. Solving this equation requires finding out which values x can take in order for $f(x)$ to equal 0. In this case, x can either be -2 or 1. One way to show this is to use a technique known as solving by radicals (square roots, cube roots, etc). Galois's work, which is now known as Galois theory, showed that if the highest exponent of x in the polynomial was 5 or higher, a solution could never be found using radicals.

As well as his mathematical genius, Galois was also a political firebrand during a tumultous time in French history. During the 1830 July Revolution, Galois was arrested and imprisoned for his part in a protest. He would die less than two years later, shot in the abdomen during a duel.

▲ The work of Évariste Galois (1811–1832) on the exponents of polynomial functions formed the basis of what is now known as Galois theory.

20

Maximum number of moves required to solve a Rubik's cube

In 1974, a Hungarian professor of architecture created one of the most successful toys in history. Erno Rubik's eponymous cube took the world by storm, adding up to sales of more than 350 million. And yet the cube had one stubborn puzzle that refused to be solved: the maximum number of moves needed to complete it from any starting configuration. It came to be known as "God's number." The reason this question was originally so thorny is the sheer number of different possible ways to arrange the cube at the beginning of the game—a staggering 43 quintillion (43,252,003,274,489,856,000 to be precise). Checking every single one of them was impossible.

However, in 2010 a group of mathematicians was able to solve the problem. They used an area of mathematics called group theory to divide the configurations up into 2.2 billion different groups, each containing 19.5 billion configurations. Then they exploited certain symmetrical properties of the cube to further reduce the groups to 56 million (again, each with 19.5 billion configurations). The team used computer algorithms to search through the configurations at the rate of 1 billion a second. Their work resulted in confirmation that every single configuration can be solved in 20 moves or fewer. This improved upon a previous result from 2007, which suggested the cube could always be solved in a maximum of 26 moves.

▼ Despite having more than 43 quintillion unique starting configurations, mathematicians have shown that the Rubik's cube can always be solved in 20 moves or fewer.

23

Number of Hilbert's problems

In August 1900, German mathematician David Hilbert stood before his peers in Paris. His speech to the International Congress of Mathematicians contained a list of what he considered to be the ten biggest outstanding problems in mathematics at the time. He later published a more complete list containing 23 problems, which have come to be known as Hilbert's problems, and they would have a profound influence on the direction of mathematics over the next hundred years (and beyond).

Here are just a few of his 23 problems:

Problem 3

Given any two polyhedra of equal volume, is it always possible to cut the first into finitely many polyhedral pieces that can be reassembled to yield the second?

Remember that polyhedra are solid three-dimensional shapes made from polygons (see page 36). Examples include the cube and the tetrahedron. If you can cut a polyhedron up into smaller polyhedra, and use those to build an alternative polyhedron with the same volume as the first, mathematicians call the two large polyhedra "scissors-congruent." This problem was the first on Hilbert's list to be solved. Within a year, his student Max Dehn had provided an example of two polyhedra of equal volume that were not scissors-congruent.

David Hilbert (1862–1943)

Hilbert was born in Königsberg, and after studying mathematics he became a senior lecturer at the local university, where he stayed until 1895. He was then "poached" by Felix Klein (see page 134) and transferred to the University of Göttingen, where he remained until his death.

By that time, much of his department had been destroyed by the rise of the Nazis and their purge of Jewish academics. A prominent Nazi minister asked Hilbert at a banquet: "How is mathematics in Göttingen now that it has been freed of the Jewish influence?" Hilbert is said to have replied: "Mathematics in Göttingen? There is really none any more."

Problem 7

Is a^b always transcendental when a is algebraic and b is irrational?

A transcendental number is one that isn't algebraic, and an algebraic number is one that is the solution to a polynomial equation. Take the polynomial equation $x^2 + 2x + 1 = 0$. The value of x for which this holds is $x = -1$, therefore -1 is an algebraic number and not transcendental. Well-known examples of transcendental numbers include π (see page 30) and e (page 22).

A number is irrational if it cannot be neatly written as a fraction. Famous irrational numbers include π and e again, along with ф (see page 18) and $\sqrt{2}$ (see page 15).

This problem was solved in 1934 by Russian mathematician Alexander Gelfond and his work was refined later the same year by German Theodor Schneider, hence the solution is known as the Gelfond–Schneider theorem. It showed that a^b is always transcendental under those circumstances.

Problem 8

The Riemann hypothesis

The Riemann hypothesis involves a guess regarding how prime numbers are distributed. It remains unproven to this day and is arguably the biggest outstanding problem in mathematics. It was included in the Clay Mathematics Institute's list of Millennium Problems in the year 2000—an analogous exercise to Hilbert's in 1900 (see page 153).

Problem 18

Three separate questions on tiling and sphere packing:

a) Is the number of space groups finite?

Space groups represent the symmetry of a pattern of three-dimensional shapes. They are the number of different transformations (see page 32) you can make without changing the pattern's appearance. It was later shown there are 230 such groups (see page 87), so the answer to the question is yes.

b) Is there a polyhedron that admits only an anisohedral tiling in three dimensions?

Shapes are said to admit tiling if they can be joined together to fill up space with no gaps. If you can swap any of the tiles without altering the overall pattern, the tiling is said to be "isohedral." If you can't do this, the tiling is called "anisohedral." German mathematician Karl Reinhardt solved this problem in 1928 by finding an anisohedral tiling.

c) What is the maximum amount of empty space you can fill by packing spheres together?

In the early 1600s, German astronomer Johannes Kepler had suggested that, if you tried to fill a cube up with spheres, the maximum amount of space those spheres would take up inside the box was 74%. This remained unsolved until recently, when Thomas Hales finally proved the Kepler conjecture (see page 74).

30

Number of MacMahon cubes

Percy Alexander MacMahon was born in Malta in 1854 and would go on to have a joint career in the military and mathematics, specializing in "combinatorics"—a field that deals with how to combine objects according to certain constraints. As part of this work, he came up with a set of special cubes.

Imagine a standard cube with its six faces. How many ways are there to color in the cube so that each face has a unique color? The answer is 30.

Let's use the colors red, blue, green, yellow, black, and white and label each face from 1 to 6. What is possible if face 1 is always red? The table below shows the possible combinations.

Because no color can appear on two faces, no color can appear in the same row or column of our table. So we start by filling in the first column and first row with the rest of the colors in order. Completing the rest of the table is like finishing a Sudoku puzzle.

So there are five possible ways of coloring the cube if face 1 is always red. If we redrew the table with face 1 always being blue, we'd get five more combinations. Because face 1 can have six different colors, that's 6 x 5 combinations, or 30.

▲ Percy Alexander MacMahon (1854-1929) spent a lot of his time working on the mathematical field of combinatorics and came up with the MacMahon cubes.

Face					
1	Red	Red	Red	Red	Red
2	Blue	Green	Yellow	Black	White
3	Green	Blue	White	Yellow	Black
4	Yellow	Black	Blue	White	Green
5	Black	White	Green	Blue	Yellow
6	White	Yellow	Black	Green	Blue

30.1

Frequency with which
1 appears as the first digit in
many large lists of numbers (%)

In any large list of numbers, you'd expect the first digit of each number to be pretty random. With nine possible digits (1–9), you might expect an 11.1% chance of finding each one at the start of a number. However, in 1938, American physicist Frank Benford discovered that 1 appears first 30.1% of the time in certain types of number lists. The frequency of subsequent digits continues to decline until 9 appears first on just 4.6% of occasions.

This strange quirk has become known as Benford's law. The Canadian-born American astronomer Simon Newcomb actually hit upon it first in 1881 as he was thumbing through a book of logarithms (see page 104) and noticed that pages starting with 1 were more worn than the others.

However, there are some caveats. Benford's law doesn't hold for a truly random set of numbers. Take a lottery. If balls or tickets beginning with 1 were drawn more frequently, mathematicians would be raking it in by now. Nor does it work for number lists that are too "constrained." If you looked at height in meters of everyone on Earth, almost all numbers will start with 1.

This means Benford's law can be used to look for irregularities in nonrandom number lists that aren't too constrained. Studies have shown, for example, that the numbers in tax returns follow the law and so forensic accountants can use it to look for fraud. In 2009, one Polish mathematician used Benford's law to suggest the Iranian election results of that year were rigged.

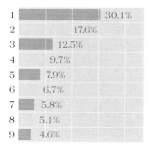

1	30.1%
2	17.6%
3	12.5%
4	9.7%
5	7.9%
6	6.7%
7	5.8%
8	5.1%
9	4.6%

▲ The frequency with which numbers 1–9 appear as the leading digit in certain types of number lists, according to Benford's law.

31

Sum of the first five rows of Pascal's triangle

One of the most famous shapes in mathematics is known as Pascal's triangle, after seventeenth-century French mathematician Blaise Pascal. It is constructed using one number in the first row, two in the second, three in the third, etc. Traditionally, however, the top row is referred to as "row zero" and the next row as "row one." The edges are always equal to 1 and the values of the other numbers are calculated by adding together the two numbers above it to the left and right.

Hidden away within this seemingly simple setup are many mathematical quirks, patterns, and properties. Take, for instance, the diagonal that begins with the first entry in row two: 1, 3, 6, 10, 15, 21, etc. These are the triangle numbers (see page 48). Add any consecutive numbers in that diagonal together and you get the square numbers (1, 4, 9, 16, 25, ...). If you add up the numbers in each row, you get the sequence 1, 2, 4, 8, 16, 32, ... This is a geometrical sequence where each term is doubling in size each time (see page 158).

▼ Pascal's triangle. A relatively simple mathematical construct, hidden away with it are many of the most familiar patterns in mathematics.

Pascal and probability

Another powerful application of Pascal's triangle is its link to probability. If you look at the outcomes of tossing a varying numbers of coins, you see those numbers appear again.

Number of coins	Possible results	In number form
1	H T	1, 1
2	HH TH, HT TT	1, 2, 1
3	HHH HHT, HTH, THH TTH, THT, HTT TTT	1, 3, 3, 1
4	HHHH HHHT, HHTH, HTHH, THHH HHTT, TTHH, THTH, HTHT, HTTH, THHT TTTH, TTHT, THTT, HTTT TTTT	1, 4, 6, 4, 1

▲ French mathematician Blaise Pascal (1623–1662) laid the foundation for the modern theory of probabilities.

These same values also appear in what mathematicians call the binomial expansion. Let's see what happens when you expand out $(x+1)^y$ for different values of y:

Value of y	Expansion of $(x+1)y$
2	$(x+1)^2 = 1x^2 + 2x + 1$
3	$(x+1)^3 = 1x^3 + 3x^2 + 3x + 1$
4	$(x+1)^4 = 1x^4 + 4x^3 + 6x^2 + 4x + 1$

You'll notice that for each binomial expansion you start with the same power ("exponent") of x that the parentheses were originally raised to, before consecutively adding terms with the exponent decreasing by 1 each time. Pascal's triangle tells you the number ("coefficient") to put in each term. (You don't normally need to write 1 as a coefficient in front of x; here it's to illustrate the point.)

Pascal's triangle and circles

Pascal's triangle is also linked to the circle. First, place an increasing number of equally spaced points on the circumference of a circle. Then note the number of points used, the number of lines connecting them, and the number of triangles, quadrilaterals, pentagons, and hexagons formed inside the circle. You'll see a familiar pattern emerge pretty quickly.

Image	Points	Lines	Triangles	Quadrilaterals	Pentagons	Hexagons
	1					
	2	1				
	3	3	1			
	4	6	4	1		
	5	10	10	5	1	
	6	15	20	15	6	1

42

The 5th Catalan number

When it comes to the number 42, many people's minds are immediately drawn to the answer to the ultimate question of the meaning of life, the universe, and everything in Douglas Adams's *The Hitchhiker's Guide to the Galaxy*. While the question is not revealed, a possible (if unlikely) candidate would be: "What is the 5th Catalan number?"

Named after Belgian mathematician Eugène Catalan (1814–1894), the Catalan numbers are a sequence that crops up time and again when trying to tackle different mathematical problems.

One way to think about them is to imagine strangers seated at a round banquet table. For the sake of politeness, everyone wants to shake hands with one of their dinner companions but nobody wants to reach over another pair of hands to do so. When you think about the different ways this is possible, you quickly realize it will never work unless you have an even number of guests. Otherwise one person will be left with no one's hand to shake.

We can then start to look at the number of permutations with an even numbers of guests. With two people, there is only one way to proceed: they shake each other's hand. With four people, the answer is 2—you can shake the hand of the person to your left and right, but not the person diagonally opposite you. For six people it is 5, for eight people 14, and it's 42 ways for ten dinner guests.

Thus begins the Catalan sequence of numbers: 1, 2, 5, 14, 42 …

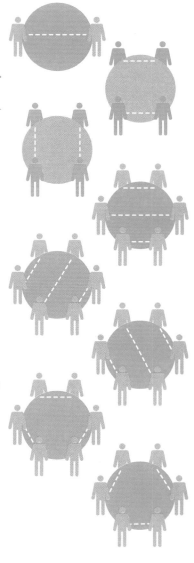

▲ To visualize the Catalan numbers, imagine the ways an increasingly even number of guests can shake hands around a circular table without crossing arms.

60

Number of seconds
in a minute

Have you ever wondered why we have 60 seconds in a minute? After all, we use base-10 for most other things (see page 43), so why not split minutes (and hours) up into divisions of 10 instead?

It is because we inherited our time system from the ancient Babylonians, who instead used a sexagesimal system. They counted in base-60.

Using 60 as your base number can be particularly useful, because 60 divides equally by many numbers (1, 2, 3, 4, 5, 6, 10, 12, 15, 20, 30, and 60) and so calculating fractions is much easier than with 10 (which only divides by 1, 2, 5, and 10).

The French mathematical historian Georges Ifrah believes it might also have something to do with our fingers. Look at your right hand with your palm facing you. You'll notice that your four fingers are each divided into three sections (called phalanges)—that's 12 on your right hand. To see how Ifrah believes this was of use, take the four fingers on your left hand and imagine that your left index finger represents 12, your left middle finger is 24, the ring finger is 36, and the pinkie is 48.

Your two hands can then be used to show any number between 1 and 60. To show 44, for example, point to the middle section of your right middle finger (the eighth phalange) using your left ring finger. That's 36 for the left ring finger and 8 for the phalange, or 44.

▼ It's possible we divide time into chunks of 60 because it is easy to depict any number between 1 and 60 using our two hands.

61

Number of people you need for a 99.5% chance that two of them share a birthday

The Birthday paradox belongs to a series of mathematical problems that include the Monty Hall problem (see page 68) and the Rope Around the World puzzle (see page 39)—it challenges our common-sense ideas.

Imagine you're in a room with 60 other people and you want to know if any two people share a birthday. What are the chances? Here's where our intuition can fool us. There are 365 days in nonleap years, and so you might say that there is a 1/365 chance of anyone being born on a particular day, and with 61 people to choose from you might come up with an answer of 61/365—or just over 17%. And yet the answer is 99.5%. This is because it isn't just whether someone shares a birthday with you, but if any two people were born on the same day.

Do the math

We can find an approximate answer by pairing up every person in the room with every other person exactly once and cross-checking their birthdays. With 61 people in the room, that means that each person has to be checked against 60 other people. Of course, checking Jack's birthday with Jill's is the same as checking Jill's birthday with Jack's, so we need to be careful not to count every check twice. So the total number of checks needed is: (61 x 60)/2 = 1,830. Dividing by 2 is what prevents us from checking everyone twice. That means there are actually 1,830 chances of a shared birthday. You could check all 1,830 possibilities by asking people; however, it is simpler to approximate it using math.

The probability of any one pair having a matching birthday is 1/365. So the probability that they don't have a matching birthday is 364/365. To estimate the chances that no one in the room shares a birthday, we raise 364/365 to the power of 1,830 (the number of pairs to check). That's $(364/365)^{1830}$. Plugging this into a calculator gives 0.0066 (to four decimal places). So, according to this rough-and-ready method, there is just a 0.66% chance that no one in the room shares a birthday. That's a 99.3% chance that they do. (Note: If you this work out in a more rigorous way to find the exact answer, it is 99.5%.)

In fact, you only need a group of 23 people to be sure of a 50% probability that two people in the room will share a birthday.

The only catch here is that we have assumed people have an equal probability of being born on any day of the year. In practice it doesn't quite work like that. In the northern hemisphere, for example, more children are born in the summer months, perhaps due to increased conception rates during the colder months and the influence of Christmas and New Year. These variations actually make it even more probable to find matches in large groups. It just goes to show that human brains are not good at grappling with probabilities on the spur of a moment.

▼ The chances of two people in a small group blowing out their birthday candles on the same day is a lot greater than many of us intuitively think.

65

Number of solutions to a
pentomino tessellation problem

The computer game Tetris is one of the most popular of all time, regularly appearing near the top of lists ranking the world's greatest games. First released in 1984, it has since sold hundreds of millions of copies.

The aim of the game is to marshal different falling shapes into a complete block at the bottom of the screen without any gaps. Mathematicians call this combination of shapes with no overlaps or gaps "tessellation." In Tetris, there are seven shapes in total, each made of four squares joined together edge to edge—a shape mathematicians call a "tetromino." The Russian inventor of the game, Alexey Pajitnov, combined this word with his favorite sport—tennis—to come up with the game's name.

Tetrominoes form part of a larger family of shapes known as polyominoes, which are built using various numbers of joined squares. Although they probably date back to antiquity, polyominoes were brought to wider attention by Solomon W. Golomb (b. 1932) in his 1965 book *Polyominoes: Puzzles, Patterns, Problems, and Packings*. One of the most popular

▼ The shapes in the popular computer game Tetris are known as tetrominoes and form part of a larger group of shapes called polyominoes.

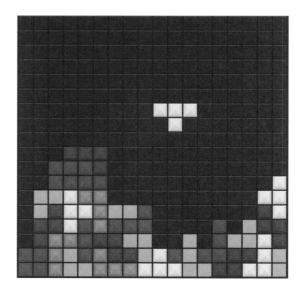

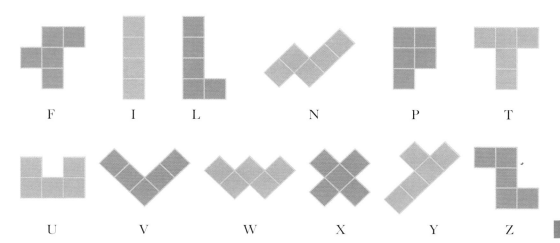

F   I   L   N   P   T

U   V   W   X   Y   Z

polyominoes for mathematical puzzles is the pentomino, made from five squares. It is possible to make 12 unique pentominoes—a nice, manageable number (the next polyomino up, the six-square hexomino, has a slightly excessive 35 variations). They are given labels based on the letters of the alphabet they resemble: F, I, L, N, P, T, U, V, W, X, Y, and Z.

A popular pentomino puzzle is to tessellate the shapes in a similar way to the game of Tetris—that is, fill up a rectangle with all 12 shapes so that there are no gaps. Because the 12 shapes each have five squares, the total area of the rectangle needs to be 60 squares. That could be a 12 × 5 grid, a 6 × 10 one, or any other suitable combination. In the first two cases, there are 1,010 and 2,339 possible solutions. However, for the 3 × 20 rectangle, there are only two.

One way to simplify the game is to try to fit the pentominoes into an 8 × 8 grid that has a 2 × 2 hole missing in the middle (that's still 60 spaces). How many different solutions are there to this puzzle? As far back as 1958, American computer scientist Dana Scott (b. 1932) showed the answer to be 65.

66.7

Chance of winning if you switch doors in the Monty Hall problem (%)

Sometimes common sense deceives us. What seems at first to be obvious can often be shown to be wrong by mathematical reasoning. One of the most famous examples of this phenomenon is the Monty Hall problem, named after a famous American game show host.

Imagine a TV competition in which the player is confronted with three closed doors. Hidden behind the doors are two goats and one car, but the contestant is not told which object is behind which door. They are then asked to select a door to open, winning whatever prize is revealed behind it. So far so good, but then comes the twist. Once the contestant has selected their door, the host steps in. Knowing what is behind the doors, he immediately opens one of the doors hiding a goat. The host then offers the contestant the chance to change from their original choice to the other unopened door.

If you were the contestant faced with this game, what would you do? By far the most common answer given is to stick with your original choice. Their logic is that the odds of winning the car are now 50:50, so sticking gives you as good a chance as any and you'll only be frustrated if you swapped after having picked the car from the outset. Yet that's not the way to go. You actually only have a 33.3% chance of winning if you stick, but you have a 66.7% chance if you switch.

Perhaps the easiest way to see why is to draw on an area of mathematics called "game theory," made famous by the 2001 movie *A Beautiful Mind.* One of the tools of game theory is a "payoff matrix," effectively a grid showing all possible outcomes of some competition.

Below is the payoff matrix for the Monty Hall problem, assuming you originally pick Door 1. Remember the host always opens a door to reveal a goat.

There are three possible ways the prizes could have been distributed behind the doors. By working through the game, you can see that in two out of the three scenarios you win the car by switching. Sticking only wins you the car in one-third of occasions. There is nothing special about picking Door 1 to start with either. If you work out the results of switching and sticking having started with Doors 2 or 3, you get the same probabilities.

The fault in the original logic comes from the incorrect assumption that because two doors are left, the odds of success must be 50:50. You had a 33.3% chance of picking the car from the outset and that doesn't change just because the host has opened one of the other doors. But by switching, you are utilizing the knowledge that the host has introduced into the game. As all probabilities must add up to 100%, there is now a 66.7% chance the car is behind the other door. You should switch.

▲ The Monty Hall problem, with its three doors, has confounded many. Even when it was first formulated, people with doctorates were incorrectly claiming it was wrong.

Door 1	Door 2	Door 3	Host opens	What you get if you stick	What you get if you switch
Goat	Goat	Car	Door 2	Goat	Car
Car	Goat	Goat	Door 2 or 3	Car	Goat
Goat	Car	Goat	Door 3	Goat	Car

68

Amount of normally distributed data lying within one standard deviation of the mean (%)

Sets of data can be spread out in many different ways. It could be that the majority of the data sit above the mean, but they could equally sit below it. However, in large data sets, the points often settle equally on either side. Plotted on a graph, the shape of the distribution resembles a bell, so is sometimes referred to as a "bell curve." It is also known as the "normal distribution" or "Gaussian distribution," after German mathematician Carl Friedrich Gauss.

Johann Carl Friedrich Gauss (1777–1855)

Born in Germany, Gauss would go on to be regarded as "The Prince of Mathematicians." In turn, he would call mathematics "The Queen of the Sciences." We'll see later (page 142) just how precocious a talent he was, even from an early age. In fact, he would use math to work out his own birthday. His mother was illiterate and never documented the exact date of his birth—she could only recall it in relation to Easter. Because Easter is a festival based on the lunar calendar, its date changes every year. So, at the age of 22, Gauss devised a method for calculating the date of Easter Sunday for any year, past or future. In doing so, he finally revealed his birthday as being on April 30.

His involvement with all things astronomical continued in the early nineteenth century. In 1801, the asteroid Ceres had been discovered and was at first called a planet. However, the astronomer who found it, Giuseppe Piazzi, soon lost sight of it. Gauss was able to use his previous observations to correctly calculate where Ceres should be, and the study of what is now regarded as a dwarf planet was able to continue.

Setting the standard

One of the key features of a normal distribution is related to a statistical measurement known as the standard deviation. It's all about spread. We'll see on page 98 that you can get a sense of where the middle of a data set is by taking an average. But how tightly clustered around this average are the rest of the data points? Take the following two sets of numbers:

1, 2, 3, 4, 17, 20, 23

8, 9, 9, 10, 10, 10, 14

They both add up to 70, and they both contain 7 numbers, so the mean value of both sets is 10. However, you can see that the numbers in the first set are much more spread out than those in the second set. That's where standard deviation can help.

The formula for calculating the standard deviation can often look daunting at first. However, it's not actually that bad.

$$SD = \sqrt{\frac{\Sigma(x - \bar{x})^2}{n}}$$

Where x is a number in the list, $\bar{x}$ is the mean, n is the total number of entries in the list and Σ is the Greek letter sigma, which mathematicians use to represent adding everything together.

What it is asking you to do is work out how much each data point varies from the mean, square that answer, and find the average of all those answers. This value is called the variance. If you then take the square root, you get the standard deviation. We show here the calculation for our first list of numbers.

We divided 548 by the amount of numbers in the list (7) to get a variance of 78.3. Square rooting that tells us that the standard deviation is 8.8. Repeating the same process for the second set of numbers would yield a standard deviation of just 1.8. The lower the standard deviation, the more the data points are clustered around the mean.

Calculating the variance

x	$x\text{-}\bar{x}$	$(x\text{-}\bar{x})^2$
1	-9	81
2	-8	64
3	-7	49
4	-6	36
17	7	49
20	10	100
23	13	169
	Total	548

548 divided by 7 = 78.3

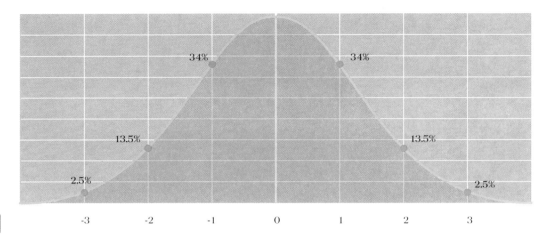

		34%	34%			
	13.5%				13.5%	
2.5%						2.5%

-3   -2   -1   0   1   2   3

What's this got to do with normal distribution? Well, if a data set is normally distributed, then 68% of all the data points will fall within one standard deviation on each side of the mean. Around 95% will fall within two standard deviations.

Such statistics are particularly powerful when taking information about a small subset of a population and using it to infer things about the population as a whole. For example, it is important to keep track of fish stocks in the ocean, yet it is hardly practical to count every creature. Because the overall population of fish is thought to be normally distributed, by catching a sample of fish, you can use statistics to fill in the rest of the information.

▲ A graph of normally distributed data—known as a "bell curve"—showing how the data is clustered around the mean. The x-axis shows multiples of standard deviation.

70

Smallest weird number

Numbers come in all kinds of varieties. They can be odd and even, perfect and weird. A weird number is one in which the numbers that divide into it (except itself) add up to more than the number itself and yet no subset of those numbers add up to it. As always, this is best seen with an example.

Take the number 70. It can be divided by 1, 2, 5, 7, 10, 14, and 35, which add together to make 74. This makes 70 what is known as an abundant number—its divisors sum up to more than itself. Because none of those divisors can be added together to make 70, that also makes it "weird." A number can also be abundant but not weird. Twelve, for example, can be divided by 1, 2, 3, 4, and 6, and yet 6+4+2 = 12, so it cannot be classified as weird.

The next weird number after 70 is 836. Its divisors are 1, 2, 4, 11, 19, 22, 38, 44, 76, 209, and 418, which sum up to 844. However, there is no possibility of making 836 by adding together any of those numbers.

Mathematicians have been able to show that there is an infinite number of weird numbers, but as yet they have been unable to definitively prove that there can't be any odd weird numbers.

74

Maximum amount of space that spheres can take up in a box (%)

We've all been there. You're off on vacation and can't get your clothes to fit into your suitcase, so you take everything out and try a more efficient method—perhaps you stuff your socks into your shoes. Such "packing problems" have fascinated mathematicians for centuries. Back in 1611, the German astronomer and mathematician Johannes Kepler was pondering the most efficient way to pack spheres into a cube. He was in correspondence with fellow mathematician and astronomer Thomas Harriot, who himself had been tasked by famous explorer Sir Walter Raleigh to discover the optimum way to stack cannonballs on a ship.

Kepler's intuition

It turns out you can do a pretty good job by randomly throwing the spheres into the box. On average, this method will fill up 65% of the space. But can you do any better? Kepler found another way, suggesting the optimum setup is to do exactly what grocers have long been doing with oranges—start the bottom layer in the shape of a triangle or hexagon and place the next layers of spheres in the gaps created by the layer below. Kepler calculated that filling a cube with spheres in this way would fill $\pi/(3\sqrt{2})$, or 74%, of the space. This became known as the Kepler conjecture.

However, proving there was no better configuration was one of the longest standing problems in mathematics. In 1831, Carl Friedrich Gauss (see page 70) proved it was indeed the best

▲ Best known as an astronomer, Johannes Kepler (1571–1630) also worked on mathematics. His conjecture about packing spheres remained unconfirmed for centuries.

configuration if the spheres had to be arranged in a regular pattern. Yet what was to say there wasn't some seemingly more haphazard way to arrange them that achieved a denser packing? By the turn of the twentieth century, the problem remained unsolved and was included in David Hilbert's list of the biggest unanswered questions in mathematics (see page 54).

A modern insight

The next breakthrough came in 1953, when the Hungarian mathematician László Fejes Tóth provided a way of checking all possible arrangements of spheres, although at the time this involved far too many calculations to be practicable. He suggested that one day a powerful enough computer could check them all. In 1958, English mathematician Claude Ambrose Rogers showed the maximum value could not be more than 78%, but found no solution between Kepler's and this upper limit.

In 1990, Wu-Yi Hsiang claimed to have proved the Kepler conjecture. However, commentators including Gábor Fejes Tóth (László's son), were skeptical, and most mathematicians still regard Hsiang's proof as incomplete. By 1998, Thomas Hales released a proof containing 250 pages and 3GB of computer programs—the digital solution predicted by Fejes Tóth Snr. A panel of 12 reviewers said they were 99% certain the proof was correct.

Hales has since worked to eliminate that last 1% of doubt. In 2003, he started the Flyspeck project, using computers to churn through the proof. In January 2015, his team published a formal proof of the Kepler conjecture. Four hundred years after Kepler first suggested it, we now know he was right.

▼ Kepler suggested the optimum way to pack spheres into a cube was to copy the way grocers stacked oranges—known in mathematics as hexagonal close packing.

90

Degrees in a right angle

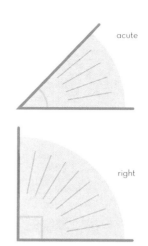

acute

right

obtuse

The properties of a right triangle are well documented. The relationship between the lengths and the other angles are described by the Pythagorean theorem (see page 15) and the SOH CAH TOA rule (see page 28).

The easiest way to create a right angle is to cut a straight line in half. It is also a quarter turn in a circle and is denoted by the symbol L. However, Thales's theorem—named after ancient Greek mathematician Thales of Miletus—gives another way to create a right angle. It says that if a triangle ABC is drawn inside the circumference of a circle, so that the side AC is also the diameter of the circle, then the angle at B will be a right angle. In keeping with the traditions of Pythagoreanism, it is said that Thales sacrificed an ox in an act of thanksgiving for this discovery. His work is mentioned in Euclid's famous work *Elements* (see page 37).

Other types of angles are classified based on their relationship to the right angle:

ACUTE Less than a right angle (<90°).

OBTUSE More than one right angle (>90°) but less than two (<180°).

STRAIGHT ANGLE Equal to exactly two right angles (=180°).

REFLEX ANGLE Greater than two right angles (>180°).

straight

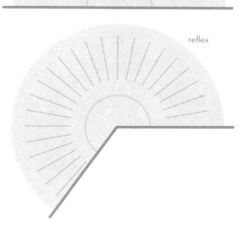

reflex

100

Number of digits in the first RSA number

The Internet has revolutionized the world of shopping. You can now browse virtual shelves from the comfort of your own living room, and getting your groceries no longer requires trudging around the refrigerator aisle—with a click of a mouse you can have someone bring your weekly shopping to your front door.

However, this convenient world of e-commerce has a drawback: a higher chance of criminals intercepting your payment details and using them to make fraudulent purchases. For online shopping to work, there needs to be a way of keeping your credit card information hidden from prying eyes, and currently this is done using prime numbers.

We saw on page 44 that the art of encoding and decoding secret information—known as cryptography—has been going on for millennia. Yet those ancient means of encryption just aren't up to the job in the modern world.

Keeping us safe online

When you log onto a web site, your browser displays a symbol to tell you the site is genuine and that your connection is secure. Depending on your browser, this is normally either a locked padlock or a green strip (it can appear either before or after the address of the page you are on). Clicking on this symbol will give you more information about how securely you are connected to the page.

If you're told that your connection to the site is encrypted, it is almost certainly using Public Key (PK) encryption. This system was devised in secret at the British Government Communications Headquarters (GCHQ) in 1973. However, because it was being used for covert government work, GCHQ only revealed they had invented it in 1997. So, instead, it is more widely known as the RSA system after the surnames of Ron Rivest, Adi Shamir, and Leonard Adleman, who came up with a similar system in 1977 but were able to talk about it freely.

The issue with the traditional means of encryption is that you also have to send information about how to decode the message: a key. Imagine that you weren't encoding a message at all, but simply locked your letter away in a box. For the recipient to be able to open the box, they will at some point need to be given the key. If the messenger unscrupulously makes a copy of the key on the way to delivering your message, they'll be able to read all your future messages, too. If you had one key to lock the box and another to open it, suddenly your communication channel would become much safer. That's exactly how PK encryption works—it has two keys, a "public key" and a "private key."

◀ A padlock next to the address bar in an Internet browser signifies that your connection is secure. The form of encryption used is based on prime numbers.

If I want you to send me a message, I will give you my public key, which you will need to use to encipher it. Yet the only way to decipher your message is using my private key, which I never divulge so no one can copy it. The keys are generated by multiplying two large prime numbers together to get a bigger number. The ingeniousness of this system lies in the fact that if you are only given the bigger number, it is extremely hard to guess what the original two prime numbers were. The public key is based on the large prime number, but my private key is based on the two hard-to-find smaller numbers.

Prime number keys

Imagine that my public key was 4,189. Which two prime numbers have I multiplied together in order to get it? The answer is 59 and 71, but even for a four-digit public key, that would take quite a while to work out. The first numbers used as public keys by the RSA system were 100 digits long (known as RSA-100). It took until 1991 for this code to be broken and even then it required a couple of days' worth of computer time. In 2009, it was announced that the two prime numbers forming the basis of an RSA number with 232 digits had been found, but that took two years to find and would have taken 2,000 years on a single average home computer. Today, online PK encryption typically uses 1,024-bit public keys (RSA numbers with 309 digits).

Many of us will go our entire lives happily and safely shopping online without a thought as to how our payment information is being kept safe. It is just another example of how math quietly underpins almost everything we do.

153

The smallest
narcissistic number

A number is considered narcissistic if it references itself. More accurately, if you raise each of the individual digits of a number to the power of the number of digits, you get the original number back. The lowest such number is 153, because $1^3 + 5^3 + 3^3 = 1 + 125 + 27 = 153$. Sometimes they are called Armstrong numbers, after computer programmer Michael F. Armstrong, who created an assignment for one of his classes to find this type of number.

There are only three other three-digit numbers that exhibit such behavior. They are:

$370 = 3^3 + 7^3 + 0^3 = 27 + 343 + 0$;

$371 = 3^3 + 7^3 + 1^3 = 27 + 343 + 1$;

and $407 = 4^3 + 0^3 + 7^3 = 64 + 0 + 343$.

Of course, there is no reason to stop at just three-digit numbers. The lowest four-digit narcissistic number is 1,634 because $1^4 + 6^4 + 3^4 + 4^4 = 1 + 1,296 + 81 + 256$. There are 88 narcissistic numbers in total, the longest boasting 39 digits.

Their relevance to serious mathematics has been debated for some time. In his famous book *A Mathematician's Apology*, British mathematician G. H. Hardy said of narcissistic numbers "[they] are odd facts, very suitable for puzzle columns and likely to amuse amateurs, but there is nothing in them which appeals to the mathematician."

176

The solution to the
ultimate magic square

Mathematics can be both beautiful and intriguing, and humans have been playing around with numbers for pleasure and progress for centuries. One of the oldest forms of recreational mathematics is the "magic square." As early as 650 BCE, a legend from Chinese mythology tells of a great flood. During the cleanup efforts, a king, known as Yu, was trying to divert the water back out to sea when a turtle emerged from the swell and the monarch couldn't help but notice a series of odd markings on its shell. Circular dots were arranged in a 3 x 3 grid, so that when you added up the number of dots in any column, row, or diagonal, you always arrived at the same answer: 15. This was the same as the number of days in each of the 24 cycles of a Chinese year.

This strange property defines a magic square and its sorcery continued to enchant mathematicians and nonmathematicians alike well into the Middle Ages. In 1514, renowned German artist Albrecht Dürer produced an engraving known as *Melencolia I*, depicting a winged female figure looking sad (see page 83). Etched on the wall behind her is a 4 x 4 magic square whose rows, columns, and diagonals all sum up to 34 (as do the four corner boxes and the four boxes directly in the center of the square). The year of the work even appears in the bottom row. Clearly a fan of mathematics, Dürer even included a polyhedron, thought to be a truncated rhombohedron. Other examples of magic squares in art include a different 4 × 4 grid etched into the facade of Gaudí's Sagrada Família in Barcelona, Spain.

The rows, columns, and diagonals sum up to 33—the age of Jesus when he was crucified.

There is one magic square in particular that has particularly remarkable properties (see below left).

Like the previous magic squares, all rows, columns, and diagonals add up to the same number: 176. Again, the central four squares and the four corner squares each do, too. Now for the truly magic part of this magic square. Turn this page upside down.

You should now see a completely new magic square with a top row of 11, 22, 58, and 82. Remarkably, this adds up to 176, too. As does every other row, column, and diagonal in this new, inverted square. The four corners and four centered squares also still play by the rules.

It gets even better. Find a mirror and place it alongside the first square. You will see yet another magic square reflected in it, this time with a top row of 58, 12, 81, and 25 (below right). You can play all the same tricks with this third square and everything still adds up to 176. In fact, even turning this reflected square upside down creates a unique counterpart with a top row of 28, 82, 55, and 11. Once again all components sum up to 176. Numbers can be beautiful too.

► *Melencolia I*, Albrecht Dürer's engraving of 1514. Notice the 4 x 4 magic square in the top right corner, beneath the bell.

▼ This is what you see if you place your magic square next to a mirror. Whichever way you look at it, every row, column, and diagonal adds up to the same number.

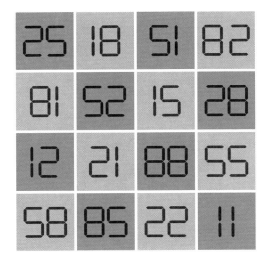

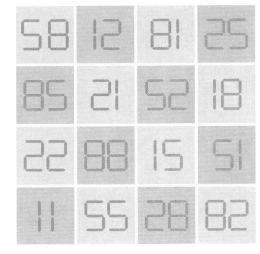

180

Degrees in a triangle

We've already seen that the angles in a triangle add up to 180° back when we looked at equilateral, isosceles, and scalene triangles (see page 24), but how can mathematicians be sure that this is the case for all triangles?

Take a look at the diagram below. The lines AB and CD are straight and parallel and there is a third straight line that cuts across them both, creating four angles at each intersection. There are rules about these angles:

VERTICALLY OPPOSITE ANGLES (so a and d, b and c, f and g, and e and h) are equal.

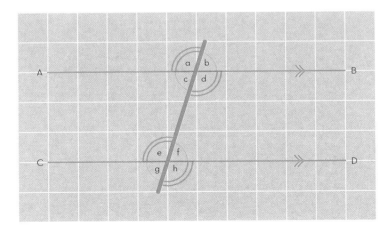

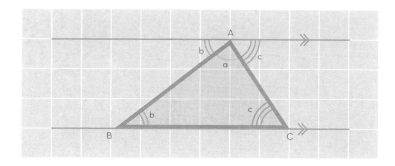

CORRESPONDING ANGLES (those in the same place in both sets) are unsurprisingly the same.

ALTERNATE ANGLES (those in each set that sit on each side of the nonparallel line, such as d and e or c and f) are also equal.

ADJACENT ANGLES (a and b, c and d, etc.) add up to 180°, because drawing an arch over both of them makes a semicircle.

INTERIOR ANGLES (those inside both lines, so d and f) also add up to 180°.

The reason this information is useful is that you can always draw two parallel lines to enclose the top and bottom of a triangle, like the ABC triangle above, with internal angles a, b, and c.

Due to the alternate angles rule, the angle a makes with the top line to its right must be equal to the angle c at the base of the triangle. Similarly, the angle a makes with the top line to its left must be equal to the angle b at the base of the triangle.

Now, because a, b, and c all sit along the same straight line at the top, they must add to 180° by the adjacent angles rule. Because these are the same angles that we find inside the triangle, the interior angles of a triangle must also add up to 180°.

This is a mathematical proof—at no point did we put any values on the lengths or angles of the triangles, so what works for this triangle must work for all triangles, as long as they can be drawn between a pair of parallel lines (which they all can).

220 & 284

The smallest pair of amicable numbers

We've already seen how certain numbers can be singled out for the unique behavior of the numbers that divide into them, and amicable numbers are no exception. Two numbers are considered amicable if their respective divisors sum up to the other number, the lowest such example being 220 and 284.

This is because 220 can be divided by 1, 2, 4, 5, 10, 11, 20, 22, 44, 55, and 110, which sum up to 284. And if you take the divisors of 284 (1, 2, 4, 71, and 142), they sum up to 220. This pair was known to the Pythagorean mathematicians, who ascribed them special mystical and astrological significance. Throughout history, other famous mathematicians chipped in with more discoveries.

It is often said Pierre de Fermat found 17,296 and 18,416 in the seventeenth century, although others suggest they were discovered centuries earlier by Arabic mathematicians. Leonhard Euler was the most prolific amicable number hunter, coming in with 59 pairs after constructing a formula to help generate them. And yet these well-known names managed to overlook the second lowest amicable pair. Only in 1866 did Italian mathematician Nicolò Paganini find 1,184 and 1,210, while still in his teens.

Modern computers have been able to find around 12 million amicable number pairs, and in all known cases both numbers must be either odd or even. It is also known that each pair must contain at least one common factor higher than 1.

230

Crystallographic space groups

In architecture, a frieze is the long, thin strip of sculpture that runs around a building, or a pattern that repeats along the top of a painting or piece of fabric. In mathematics, it has a similar meaning—it is a repeated pattern along a line. Imagine all the different shapes you could use to create a one-dimensional repeating pattern in this way. How many different translations (see page 32) could you apply to your pattern without changing its appearance? The answer is just seven.

What about going up another dimension to form a two-dimensional repeating pattern akin to the designs often found on wallpaper? This time, the number of unique ways you can apply transformations without altering the design is 17. Mathematicians call them the "wallpaper groups." They have been known about for centuries, but it took until 1891 for mathematicians to prove the list was complete. There is still no explanation for why there are 17, only that there are no more.

Of course, we don't need to stop at two dimensions. Imagine a design repeating not along a line or across a square, but within a cube. In total, there are 230 transformations—called "crystallographic space groups"—which leave the pattern looking the same. This number was arrived at in 1892, when two mathematicians—Evgraf Fedorov and Arthur Schoenflies—put together the groups they had already found independently.

▼ A wallpaper pattern using the p4mm pattern, one of only 17 distinct ways to create two-dimensional patterns so that transformations don't alter its appearance.

300 BCE

Year of Euclid's algorithm

There are many examples throughout these pages illustrating the importance of Euclid's seminal mathematical work *Elements* (see page 37). Published around 300 BCE, it also detailed a method—since known as Euclid's algorithm—for determining the greatest common denominator (GCD) of two numbers. This is the largest number that divides into both of them.

Let's say we want to determine the GCD of 513 and 837. The first step is to divide the bigger number (the "dividend") by the smaller one (the "divisor") and to look at what's left over (the "remainder"). The answer you get is 1 remainder 324—513 divides into 837 once with 324 left over. Because Euclid's algorithm only makes use of the remainder, let's introduce some new notation.

For the same division, a mathematician would write 837 mod 513 = 324, where mod stands for "modulo" and forms part of an area of mathematics called modular arithmetic. Euclid's algorithm then proceeds in a similar way, dividing the last divisor by the new remainder until eventually the resulting remainder is zero:

513 mod 324 = 189
324 mod 189 = 135
189 mod 135 = 54
135 mod 54 = 27
54 mod 27 = 0

Once you reach the point where the remainder is zero, the GCD of the two original numbers is the last divisor—that is, 27.

355

Number of mathematicians who had made errors according to 1935 book

Not everyone gets it right all the time. Mathematicians, just like everyone else, can sometimes get things wrong. In 1935, Belgian mathematician and chemist Maurice Lecat published *Erreurs de mathématiciens des origines à nos jours*, in which he details the pre-1900 errors of 355 mathematicians, some of whom are regarded as among the greatest mathematicians of all time. His self-published nit-picking exercise took up 130 pages.

Pierre de Fermat, for example, believed he had discovered a formula that always creates prime numbers. And yet, as you'll see on page 96, the number 641 showed that he was wrong. Euler, too, was fallible. According to Lecat, he believed the number 1,000,009 to be prime when in fact it can be divided by 293 and 3,413. He also published a list of 64 pairs of amicable numbers (see page 86), two of which were incorrect. Other mathematicians contained within this book who also appeared in Lecat's include Abel, Descartes, Gauss, Leibniz, Newton, and Poincaré.

In modern times, the advent of computing, and its ability to help with substantial mathematical proofs, has perhaps made it more difficult to check for and deal with errors. British mathematician Andrew Wiles's eventual proof of Fermat's last theorem (see page 138) was more than 150 pages long—longer than Lecat's book. However, an error discovered after Wiles first announced the proof in 1993 took him more than a year to correct.

360

Degrees in a circle

It may seem odd that a circle isn't divided into 100 or 1,000 smaller subdivisions. The jury is still out on why we've inherited a system with 360°. Some say it's due to the Babylonians' fondness of the sexagesimal (base-60) system (see page 63). Others argue that it is linked to the Earth's motion around the Sun—we take 365 days to complete one orbit. So the Sun creeps about a degree across the heavens with each passing day. Perhaps they picked 360 rather than 365 because it is much easier to divide into smaller chunks—365 only divides by 5 and 73, whereas 360 divides by 22 numbers, including every number up to 10, apart from 7.

The degree itself is also subdivided into smaller chunks, with 60 arcminutes to a degree and 60 arcseconds to an arcminute. However, mathematicians are just as likely to use radians as they are degrees. To form an angle equal to one radian, start at the center of the circle and draw a line to the edge (the "radius," r), then draw an "arc" by traveling along the circumference for a distance equal to the radius. Then travel back to the center to complete a "sector." The angle made at the center is equal to one radian (57.3°). As the circumference of the circle is $2\pi r$, there are 2π radians in a circle.

▼ A radian is the angle made at a circle's center when a sector is created by drawing an arc of equal length to the circle's radius.

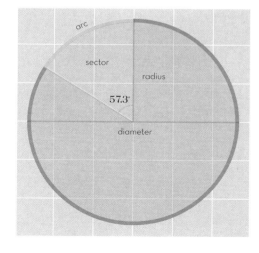

399

Lowest Lucas-Carmichael number

Named after mathematicians Édouard Lucas (see box below) and Robert Carmichael, these numbers involve looking at their divisors. They shouldn't be confused with Carmichael numbers (see page 94).

Take a number and then look at the prime numbers that divide into it. If you add 1 to each of those prime divisors and you end up with factors of the original number plus 1, then you have yourself a Lucas-Carmichael number. The lowest is 399. That's because the prime numbers that divide into 399 are 3, 7, and 19. Add 1 to each of them and you get 4, 8, and 20, which are also divisors of 400 (399 + 1). The next two Lucas-Carmichael numbers are 935 and 2,015.

Édouard Lucas (1842–1891)

Born in the French city of Amiens, François Édouard Anatole Lucas is most widely known for his study of the Fibonacci sequence (see page 18). He was also so fascinated by prime numbers that at the age of 15 he set about trying to prove, by hand, that $2^{127} - 1$ is prime. He did eventually succeed, but it took him 19 years. His also credited with inventing the popular Tower of Hanoi puzzle (see page 42). He died in 1891, at the age of 49, after attending a banquet at which a waiter accidentally smashed a plate. Some of the debris cut Lucas's cheek and several days later he died of suspected septicemia.

500CE

Invention of the decimal Hindu-Arabic numeral system

While you may think it unlikely, you are probably entirely familiar with the decimal Hindu-Arabic number system—it's the one most of us use every day. The system has ten digits (0, 1, 2, 3, 4, 5, 6, 7, 8, and 9) and was invented in India around 500 CE. Traveling Arab merchants soon spread the system west, thanks to its popularization by mathematician and astronomer Al-Khwarizmi (see box, opposite). Later, Fibonacci (see page 18) would encounter it in North Africa and spread its use to Europe. However, it was a German, Adam Ries, who is credited with its use in Europe really taking off. In his 1522 work *Rechnung auff der Linihen und Federn*, he set about teaching apprentices of businessmen and craftsmen how to perform calculations with the Hindu-Arabic numerals.

Get in position

The system Ries wrote about uses what mathematicians call "position notation" to depict a value. The position of a digit within a number denotes its magnitude—there is a hundreds column, a tens column, and a units columns, etc. The system was revolutionary, thanks to its introduction of a zero digit. Its ease and speed of calculation meant that position notation slowly replaced the previously used "sign value notation." Under this older system—an example of which is Roman numerals—you have to add together a set of numerical signs to reach the number being shown.

Al-Khwarizmi (ca. 780–ca. 850)

Thoughts differ regarding where Muslim mathematician Muhammad ibn Musa al-Khwarizmi was born. Some believe he was born in Baghdad, others in what is now Uzbekistan. What is certain, however, is his influence on Western mathematics.

In around 825 CE, he wrote a book called *On the Calculation with Hindu Numerals*, which was responsible for spreading the Hindu-Arabic number system throughout the Middle East. It was later translated into Latin under the title *Algoritmi de numero Indorum* (or "Al-Khwarizmi on the numbers of the Indians"). It is from this Latinized form of his name that we get the word "algorithm." An earlier work, *The Compendious Book on Calculation by Completion and Balancing*, was also later translated into Latin with the title *Liber Algebræ et Almucabola*, from which we get the word "algebra." He also did influential work on trigonometry, as well as linear and quadratic equations.

For example, the number 83 is written in Roman numerals as LXXXIII—you add L (50) to three Xs (3 × 10) and three Is (3 × 1).

The shapes of the digits 0–9 themselves are also of Indian origin and are descended from Brahmi numerals. There is an urban myth suggesting that the shapes of the digits are based on the number of angles required to draw them, but there is no evidence for this.

For a few centuries after the introduction of the Hindu-Arabic system, there was much disagreement between abacists (those who favored the abacus) and algorists (those who performed calculations based on a positional value system).

561

Lowest Carmichael number

Mathematicians have a special fondness for prime numbers, and they have invented various ways to check if a number is prime. One such test—known as Fermat's Little Theorem—was devised in 1640 by French mathematician Pierre de Fermat. It says that if a number, p, is prime, then $a^p - a$ will be divisible by p, where a can be any number between 1 and p itself.

We can start with an easy example and test to see if 3 is prime. $1^3 - 1 = 0$, which is divisible by 3 (0 is divisible by any whole number). Then we have $2^3 - 2 = 6$, which is divisible by 3, and $3^3 - 3 = 24$, which is also divisible by 3. So 3 comfortably passes Fermat's test for primality. And yet there are some numbers that pass this test but are actually not primes at all. These numbers are known as Carmichael numbers after American mathematician Robert Carmichael. The lowest such number is 561. So if you use Fermat's Little Theorem with p equal to 561, and run it for values of a from 1 all the way up to 561, it passes the test every time. It is not prime, however, because it can be divided by 3, 11, and 17. Due to this possibility of imposters, mathematicians now have a new way to test for primality called the AKS test, which it is claimed is 100% accurate at determining primes.

563

Highest known Wilson prime

There is another relatively straightforward way to test a number to see whether it is prime. It involves a mathematical operation known as a "factorial," which is denoted by an exclamation mark, for example 4! (said "4 factorial"). To carry out this operation, you multiply the number by every number below it until you reach 1. So 4! = 4 × 3 × 2 × 1 = 24.

A number, p, is prime if (p-1)! + 1 is divisible by p. Let's take 5 as an example. That would give us 4! + 1, which we know is equal to 24 + 1 = 25. And, of course, 25 is divisible by 5, so 5 is indeed prime. The idea that this works for every prime number and not for nonprime numbers is known as Wilson's Theorem, after eighteenth-century English mathematician John Wilson.

A Wilson prime is any prime number that passes this test twice—you can divide your answer from the theorem by the prime number a second time. Taking 5 as our example, we got 25 as our answer, which we divided by 5 to get 5. However, you can divide it by 5 again to get 1. This makes 5 the lowest Wilson prime. Only two other Wilson primes are known to exist—13 and 563. It is thought there must be more, but another is yet to be found despite checking every number up to 20 trillion.

▲ In mathematics, an exclamation mark stands for factorial. If you see it after a number, multiply that number by every positive number lower than it.

641

First counterexample of Fermat's conjecture

Like many of his colleagues, French mathematician Pierre de Fermat had a lifelong love affair with prime numbers. As part of his work, he defined a new type of number, which are now known as Fermat numbers.

They take the form $F_n = 2^{2^n} + 1$, where the list of Fermat numbers is generated by replacing n with numbers from 0 upward. The first four (using n = 0, 1, 2, and 3) are 3, 5, 17, and 257, all of which are prime. Fermat had a hunch that all such Fermat numbers were prime, offering a new way to generate prime numbers. Prime numbers generated in this way are known as Fermat primes. However, there is a catch; it soon stops working. F_5 (the sixth Fermat number) is the first number where it breaks down as $F_5 = 2^{2^5} + 1 = 2^{32} + 1 = 4,294,967,297$. In 1732, Swiss mathematician Leonhard Euler showed that this can be divided by 641 and, therefore, is not prime.

Modern mathematicians have been able to use computers to show that Fermat numbers continue to be composite (not prime) up to and including F_{32}. In July 2014, an incredibly large Fermat number, $F_{3,329,780}$ was shown to be composite, because it can be divided by $193 \times 2^{3,329,782} + 1$, a prime number so big that it has more than a million digits and is hence called a megaprime (a titanic prime has at least 1,000 digits and a gigantic prime has at least 10,000).

▲ French mathematician Pierre de Fermat (1601–1665) thought he had found a method that guaranteed to generate prime numbers, but it doesn't always work.

1,001

The test of divisibility
by 7, 11, and 13

The number 1,001 has three prime divisors—7, 11, and 13. This fact can be utilized to test whether another number is divisible by any of these three numbers.

Working out whether a small number is divisible by 7, 11, or 13 is relatively straightforward. If you know your basic times tables, for example, you might realize that numbers such as 14, 42, and 84 are all divisible by 7. But what about 3,326,505? Without a calculator, it may seem like a thankless and long-winded task. Actually, it is easier than you think.

First take the number and split it up into groups of three digits, starting from the right-hand side. So, for our number, this is 3,326,505. Add the odd groups together (that is, groups 1, 3, 5, and so on). In this case, that is 3 + 505 = 508. Then do the same for the even groups (simply 326 here, because there is only one even group).

Now subtract the even total from the odd to get 508 – 326 = 182. If this much smaller number is exactly divisible by 7, 11, or 13, then so is the original bigger number. So that tells us that 3,326,505 can be divided by 7 and 13 (because 182/7 = 26 and 182/13 = 14) but not 11 (because 182/11 = 16.5454...).

1,225

Average global
monthly salary ($)

We hear about averages a lot. "She was above average for her age"; "that was a below-par performance." Averages are all about comparing one group with another. Take, for example, the salaries of everyone on Earth—how do we get a sense of where the middle income is? Or to use the language of statisticians, how do we get "a measure of central tendency"?

Well, there isn't just one way of calculating an average—there are three, and they each have their strengths and weaknesses.

Mean

This is the average you are probably most familiar with. Given a list of numbers, add them all up, and divide that by the amount of numbers in the list.

Take the first ten numbers of the Fibonacci sequence, for example (see page 18). They are 1, 1, 2, 3, 5, 8, 13, 21, 34, and 55. The mean value of this list is therefore (1 + 1 + 2 + 3 + 5 + 8 + 13 + 21 + 34 + 55)/10 = 14.3. However, if we were to add the next number to the end of the list (89), the mean would jump to 21.1. The addition of a single big number has raised the mean considerably. Calculations of the mean are often sensitive to these "outliers" (particularly small or particularly big numbers).

Median

One way of finding an average that is less sensitive to outliers is to use the median. This literally is the middle. To find it, rearrange all the numbers in numerical order and look for the number occupying the middle position. Fortunately, our original list of ten Fibonacci numbers is already in order. Unfortunately, it contains an even amount of numbers, so the median is the value halfway between the fifth and sixth numbers. In this case, that is 6.5 (halfway between 5 and 8). This is less than half as big as the mean for the same list of numbers.

If we added 89 to the end of the list again, the new median would only rise to 8 (the sixth number occupies the middle in a list of 11). This means that, even here, the new median is less than the mean for the ten numbers alone.

For this reason, $1,225 is the median average global monthly income. If we used the mean instead, the lofty salaries of the millionaires and even billionaires would disproportionately skew things upward, providing a misleading measure of average wealth.

Mode

This is simply the most common number in the list. For the first ten numbers of the Fibonnaci sequence, the mode is 1 (the only number to appear twice). However, this is a good example of when not to use the mode as a measure of central tendency—1 appears right at the beginning of the list. Even though it is the most common number, suggesting that 1 represents the middle would be misleading.

Sometimes you'll also see "range" appear in discussions that include mean, median, and mode. The range is simply the difference between the smallest and the largest numbers in the list (54 in our case).

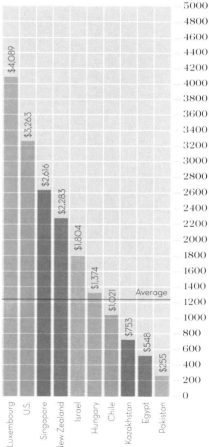

▼ The average monthly salaries of selected countries. The horizontal line represents the median world monthly salary of $1,225.

1,260

Lowest vampire number

In 1994, American computer scientist Clifford Pickover defined a new type of number, which he dubbed "vampire" numbers due to the fact they are "subtly" hidden from view. Here's how it works. Take a number with an even number of digits, say four, and split it up into two smaller numbers using those digits in any order. These two smaller numbers are called "fangs." If multiplying the two fangs together results in the original number, then that number is vampiric. The lowest number that satisfies these criteria is 1,260 because 21 x 60 = 1,260. There are six other four-digit vampire numbers: 1,395 (15 x 93), 1,435 (35 x 41), 1,530 (30 x 51), 1,827 (21 x 87), 2,187 (27 x 81), and 6,880 (80 x 86).

Longer vampire numbers can have multiple sets of fangs, such as 125,460, which can be written both as 246 x 510 and 204 x 615. You can also have "prime" vampire numbers if its fangs are both prime. Take 124,483, for example. It can be written as 281 x 443, both of which are prime numbers.

Like amicable numbers (see page 86), the mathematical value of such numbers is reasonably limited. However, like most recreational numbers (those played around with for fun), they can be a useful tool in teaching computer programming. Asking students to write a piece of code to find the list of vampire numbers was Pickover's original intention when he devised them.

1,296

(to one) Odds of rolling a Yahtzee

Yahtzee is a dice game first released in the United States in the 1940s. Players roll five dice, scoring various amounts of points for different combinations of numbers. The more unlikely the combination, the more points you get. The most you can score in a single turn is 50 points, awarded if all five dice show the same number. Such a combination is called a "Yahtzee" and the odds of hitting one rolling all five dice at once stand at 1,296 to 1.

To understand how mathematicians arrive at that number, we have to look at how to calculate probabilities for multiple events—the AND/OR rule. If you're looking for the probability that event A happens AND event B happens, you multiply the probabilities of each individual event. If you want to know the probability of event A happening OR event B happening, you add their respective probabilities together.

To roll a Yahtzee, it doesn't matter what you roll on the first die—you just want the four subsequent dice to match it. Let's say you roll a 6. The probability that you roll another 6 with die 2 is 1/6, as it is with dice 3, 4, and 5. So the overall probability is 1/6 x 1/6 x 1/6 x 1/6 or 1/1,296.

▼ In Yahtzee, five matching dice gives maximum points. The probability of achieving this in a single roll is found by multiplying the individual probabilities together.

1572

Rules for multiplying complex numbers first laid down

Of the 100 numbers in this book, mathematicians would describe all but one of them as "real." The only nonreal number is the last one—infinity. However, that doesn't mean to say all other numbers not singled out here are "real." Mathematicians also talk about "imaginary" numbers.

To see where imaginary numbers come from, it is useful to think about squaring numbers. Whenever you square a real number, you always get an answer that is positive (or zero, if you are squaring zero). For example, $4^2 = 16$, but $(-4)^2$ is also 16—even squaring negative numbers results in a positive answer. So 16 has two square roots, 4 and -4.

What if there was a number that, when squared, gave a negative answer? Said another way, what if we could calculate $\sqrt{-16}$? It is by introducing "imaginary" numbers that mathematicians are able to perform calculations like this. Under this system, $\sqrt{-1}$ is said to equal an imaginary unit called i (sometimes engineers use j, because they already use i for electrical current). So: $\sqrt{-16} = 4i$.

The power comes when you begin to multiply imaginary numbers together. Before, a calculation such as $\sqrt{-16} \times \sqrt{-9}$ may have seemed nonsensical. However, you can use imaginary numbers to find an answer. First, we can say that $\sqrt{-16} \times \sqrt{-9} = 4i \times 3i = 12i^2$. We can go a step farther by realizing from the definition of i that $i^2 = -1$ and, therefore, $\sqrt{-16} \times \sqrt{-9}$ must be equal to -12. Suddenly, the calculation has an answer that is a real number.

Mathematicians also combine real and imaginary numbers to form "complex" numbers. Complex numbers are written in the form a + bi , where the first term is called the "real part" and the second term the "imaginary part." It was the Italian mathematician Rafael Bombelli (ca. 1526–1572) who first described the rules for multiplying complex numbers in his book *L'Algebra*, published the year he died.

Say you want to multiply the complex numbers a + bi and c + di. To perform this calculation, you multiply each part of the first complex number with each part of the second. The order of these multiplications can be remembered with the pneumonic FOIL, which stands for Firsts Outers Inners Lasts.

So (a + bi)(c + di) = ac + ad$i$ + bc$i$ + bdi^2. Using the fact that i^2 = -1, we can simplify the answer to ac + ad$i$ + bc$i$ – bd. Let's try a concrete example. Multiplying out (2 + 3i)(3 + 2i) would equal (2 × 3) + (2 × 2)i + (3 × 3)i – (3 × 2) = 4i + 9i = 13i (the real parts canceled themselves out).

It is thanks to Bombelli's work that we have complex numbers today. Up until that point, no one really believed playing with imaginary numbers would have any practical use (the term "imaginary" was originally coined as an insult). Yet in modern times the manipulation of complex numbers is fundamental to physicists, engineers, and computer programmers.

▼ An example of how to use the FOIL method to multiply out two algebraic brackets. The method still works with complex numbers.

$$(3z + 5) \times (2z + 7)$$

1 Firsts $3z \times 2z = 6z^2$

2 Outers $3z \times 7 = 21z$

3 Inners $5 \times 2z = 10z$

4 Lasts $5 \times 7 = 35$

$6z^2 + 21z + 10z + 35$
$= 6z^2 + 31z + 35$

1614

John Napier first discusses logarithms

Mathematics is full of inverse operations—those that undo each other. For example, add 2 to a number and then subtract 2 and you're back to where you started. Similarly, multiplying a number by 2 and dividing it by 2 will give you the original number.

But what about raising a number to some power? How can you undo that operation? The inverse operation of an exponent (raising a number to a particular power) is called a logarithm and was first widely discussed by Scottish mathematician John Napier in 1614 (see box, opposite).

Say I have the equation $10^x = 1,000$ and I want to know the value of the exponent, x. Put another way, I want to know to what power I have to raise 10 in order to get 1,000. I would take the logarithm of both sides. Taking the logarithm of the left-hand side "undoes" the exponent and brings it "down." So I end up with $x = \log(1,000)$. Most calculators have a "log" button, (or you could look up the answer in a table of logarithms) and doing the calculation gives an answer of 3. I have to multiply 10 by itself three times to reach 1,000.

However, the log button on a calculator only deals with logarithms in base-10 (see page 43). Strictly speaking, you should always state the base you are using. In our case, that's $x = \log_{10}(1,000)$. Say instead we had $3^x = 2,187$. Following a similar method, $x = \log_3(2,187) = 7$. You couldn't use the calculator log button in this case, although you could still look it up in log tables.

John Napier (1550–1617)

The son of a Scottish laird, Napier was born in Merchiston Castle when his father was just 16 years of age. Along with inventing logarithms, he brought the decimal point into common usage. However, he was as widely known for his ingenuity as for his mathematical work.

It's said he became increasingly incensed with his neighbor's pigeons eating the seeds on his land. He warned his neighbor he'd catch the pigeons if he didn't stop them, to which the neighbor replied that if he could catch them, he could keep them. So Napier soaked peas in brandy and scattered them over the ground. The pigeons became intoxicated and Napier gathered the birds up in a sack.

He also turned his genius to catching a thief among his staff. He told them his rooster had special powers for finding out the truth. He then asked all of his workers to enter a darkened room and pet the rooster so it could see who was lying. Cunningly, however, Napier had covered the rooster in a black substance. The thief, scared he might be outed by the rooster, was the only one with clean hands afterward.

In science and engineering, Euler's number, e (see page 22), often appears raised to some power. Logarithms with base e are called natural logarithms and have their own symbol—ln. So if you had $e^x = 148.413$, you would take the natural logarithm of each side to get $x = \ln(148.413) = 5$.

1637

René Descartes first writes about Cartesian coordinates

French polymath René Descartes revolutionized mathematics in the seventeenth century by introducing a system that combined geometry and algebra in a meaningful way for the first time. His ideas are now known as Cartesian coordinates in his honor. However, there are other coordinate systems (see page 109).

René Descartes (1596–1650)

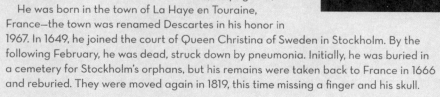

"Cogito, ergo sum"—"I think, therefore I am." Surely these are René Descartes's most famous words. He is widely considered to be the father of modern philosophy; however, he also made invaluable contributions to mathematics. As well as his work on coordinate systems, he is credited with introducing standard exponent notation—that is x^2 for x multiplied by itself. His work would be instrumental in laying the foundations for Newton and Leibniz to formulate the field of calculus (see page 112).

He was born in the town of La Haye en Touraine, France—the town was renamed Descartes in his honor in 1967. In 1649, he joined the court of Queen Christina of Sweden in Stockholm. By the following February, he was dead, struck down by pneumonia. Initially, he was buried in a cemetery for Stockholm's orphans, but his remains were taken back to France in 1666 and reburied. They were moved again in 1819, this time missing a finger and his skull.

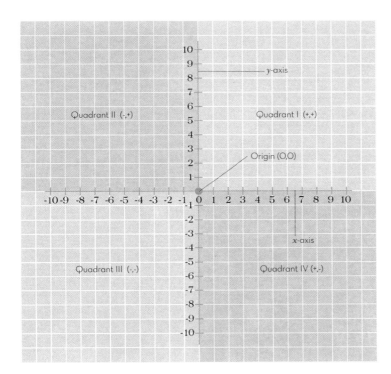

Getting to the point

In its simplest form, Descartes's system lets you specify the location of a fixed point in a two-dimensional plane. The horizontal direction is labeled as the x-axis and the vertical direction as the y-axis. The point at which the two axes meet is known as the "origin" and is sometimes denoted by the letter O. Both axes can run into positive and negative numbers, which divides the Cartesian plane into four quadrants labeled I, II, III, and IV, starting in the top right-hand side (positive x and positive y values) and moving around counterclockwise.

A particular point on a two-dimensional plane is then denoted with coordinates (x, y). The coordinate (2, 1), for example, would represent a point located two units along the x-axis and one unit up the y-axis. For points in three-dimensional space, an additional axis—the z-axis—is added and points are denoted as (x, y, z).

Part of the attraction of such a system is that shapes within the Cartesian plane can now be described by an equation and manipulated with all the usual rules of algebra. The equation $y = 5$, for example, would be a line drawn through points where $y = 5$ for every value of x (a straight, horizontal line intersecting 5 on the y-axis). The y value of a line can also change as the value of x increases. Take the line $y = 2x$. When $x = 0$, $y = 0$; when $x = 1$, $y = 2$; and $x = 2$ gives $y = 4$. So plotting the points (0, 0), (1, 2), and (2, 4) and joining them together would let me draw part of the line $y = 2x$ on the Cartesian plane.

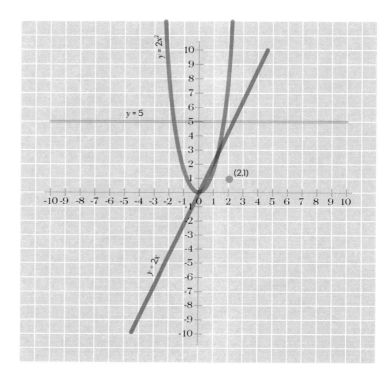

▲ Examples of some of the points, lines, and curves mentioned in the text plotted on the Cartesian plane.

Going it straight

In general, straight lines take the form $y = mx + c$, where m and c are numerical constants. Here, the m denotes the gradient (or steepness) of the line and c tells you where the line intercepts the y-axis. In our previous example of $y = 2x$, the gradient is 2 (two steps up in the y direction for every one across in the x) and c is equal to 0, because the line goes through the origin (0, 0).

It isn't just lines that can be plotted in the Cartesian plane—curves can be plotted, too. The introduction of an x^2 term leads to

what's known as a quadratic curve. The simplest example is $y = x^2$.
As a number has two square roots, there are always two values
x can have for every value of y. When $y = 1$, x can either be 1 or -1.
When $y = 4$, $x = 2$ and -2. So if you plot the points (-1, 1), (1, 1), (2, 4),
and (-2, 4), you end up with a shape known to mathematicians
as a "parabola." A parabola is always symmetrical about a
particular line (in this case, the y-axis).

In general, parabolas take the form $y = ax^2$. The larger the
value of a, the more the parabola is squeezed inward—the lower
the number, the more it expands outward. Negative values of a
will flip the parabola upside down.

Finally, circles can be drawn, too. The equation of a circle
centered on the origin (O, O) is $x^2 + y^2 = r^2$, where r is the radius of
the circle. Notice that the radius of the circle is the hypotenuse
of a right triangle with the lengths of the other two sides equal to
x and y respectively. It is no wonder, then, that the equation of the
circle takes the form of Pythagoras's rule.

Polar and spherical coordinate systems

Sometimes it is easier to denote the position of a point on a two-dimensional plane in terms
of an angle. This system, known as polar coordinates, is useful in certain fields, such as
geography and astronomy. In the Cartesian system, a point is denoted by its horizontal and
vertical distance from the origin. The equivalent of the origin in polar coordinates is known
as the "pole." The distance of a point from this pole is called the radial coordinate, or radius,
and is denoted by the letter r. The angle created between the point and some fixed line
(normally the equivalent of the horizontal x-axis) is known as the angular coordinate, or
polar angle, denoted by the Greek letter θ. So points in the Cartesian plane are written
(x, y), whereas points in the polar system are written (r,θ).

You can interchange between Cartesian and polar coordinates by utilizing the
trigonometric functions (see page 27). The x value is equal to r cos θ and the y value is
equal to r sin θ. The three-dimensional version of polar coordinates is known as spherical
coordinates with points denoted by (r,θ,φ), where φ is known the "azimuthal" angle.

1690

First use of the word "integral" to describe the area under a curve

René Descartes revolutionized geometry with the introduction of the Cartesian coordinate system (see page 106) and we've seen how it can be used to graph different mathematical functions. A related problem is determining the size of the area underneath a curve. This question forms part of a field called "calculus," from the Greek word for "small pebble." We'll see shortly there was fierce debate between English mathematician Sir Isaac Newton and German Gottfried Leibniz over who developed calculus first.

What's clear, however, is that the first person to use the word "integral" to describe the area under a curve was Swiss mathematician Jacob Bernoulli in 1690. Integration is a key part of modern calculus. Strictly speaking, the area under a curve between two specified points is referred to as the definite integral.

It is written in the form:

$$\int_{b}^{a} f(x)\, dx$$

Its solution tells you the area under the curve described by f(x) on the x-axis between points a and b ("the limits").

Let's take an example. Say you wanted to find the area under the curve described by $f(x) = x^2 - 2x + 2$ between $x = 0$ and $x = 2$ (see the graph, right).

First you would write:

$$\int_{0}^{2} f(x^2 - 2x + 2)\, dx$$

▼ You can find the area under a curve through the process of integration. The word "integral" was first coined by Jacob Bernoulli.

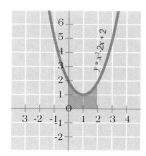

To integrate, you raise the power ("exponent") of x in each term in the parentheses and divide the answer by that new power. In the case of a number without an x, think of it as already being multiplied by x^0 (= 1) so raising it to x^1 (= x) introduces an x. You write the answer inside brackets, this time placing the limits on the right-hand side:

$$\left[\frac{x^3}{3} - x^2 + 2x \right]_0^2$$

Finally, you calculate the value of the brackets when $x = 2$ and when $x = 0$ (the limits), subtracting the second answer from the first. That is:

$$\left(\frac{8}{3} - 4 + 4 \right) - 0 = \frac{8}{3} \text{ units}^2$$

Going the other way

The opposite of integration is "differentiation" and the differential of $f(x)$ is normally written as $f'(x)$ or as $d/dx\ f(x)$.

Let's say we wanted to differentiate the function that was the result of our previous integration. That should get us back to $x^2 - 2x + 2$.

To find $f'(x)$, you multiply each term in $f(x)$ by its exponent and then you lower that exponent by 1.

So, if $f(x) = \frac{x^3}{3} - x^2 + 2x$ then $f'(x) = x^2 - 2x + 2$

Differentiation is the study of the rate of change. For example, the gradient of a parabola is always changing—at some points it climbs more steeply than at others. To find the steepness of a curve at any particular point, differentiate the function describing the curve and plug in the value of the point you're interested in.

Say you wanted to know how steep the curve $f(x) = x^2 - 2x + 2$ is at the point $x = 2$. First you find $f'(x)$, which is $2x - 2$. Then plug in $x = 2$ to get the answer 2. So at this point, the curve climbs two units in the y direction for every unit it moves to the right in the x direction.

▼ The opposite of integration is differentiation. Calculating the differential gives you the equation of the line that is tangential to the curve.

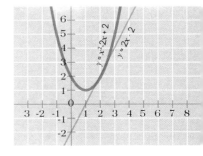

1712

Newton and Leibniz scuffle
over the invention of calculus

Calculus is the study of change and is one of the most important areas in mathematics, widely used in science, engineering, and economics. But who invented it? At the turn of the eighteenth century, there was a dispute between Englishman Isaac Newton and German Gottfried Leibniz, culminating in the publication of a document entitled *Commercium Epistolicum* in 1712, in which Newton's allies laid out their evidence. Newton claimed to have invented calculus as far back as 1666, but the manuscript containing the work was never published during his lifetime,

Sir Isaac Newton (1642–1727)

One of the most famous names in scientific history, Isaac Newton was born prematurely and just three months after the death of his father. He would later hold the prestigious title of Lucasian Professor of Mathematics at Cambridge.

Leibniz wasn't the only colleague he had a vendetta against—he almost wrote Robert Hooke out of history when he criticized his work on light and color. Newton never married and dabbled with religion and alchemy alongside traditional scientific pursuits, such as optics. He died at the age of 84 and is buried in Westminster Abbey in London.

Gottfried Leibniz (1646–1716)

Leibniz was born in the German city of Leipzig. Like Newton, his father died when Gottfried was young (six). The two men also had alchemy in common—Leibniz's first job was as secretary to an alchemical society in Nuremberg. He would later work on formal logic (what would later be called Boolean algebra; see page 126), topology, physics, and philosophy.

Just like his adversary, Leibniz never married. Toward the end of his life, he fell out of favor with many royal courts—perhaps due to his unfair reputation as a plagiarizer—and his death in Hanover at the age of 70 passed unceremoniously. His grave remained unmarked for more than 50 years.

whereas Leibniz's first work on calculus was published in 1684. Then, in 1687, Newton published the *Principia* containing groundbreaking discoveries, including his universal law of gravitation and three laws of motion, many of which he had used calculus to arrive at (although Newton called it his "method of fluxions").

Publishing after Leibniz made it look like the German had come up with calculus first. Even today, we still use the notation that Leibniz invented, including the $\int$ symbol for integration (see page 110). Newton's accusation was essentially that Leibniz was ripping off his earlier work and just using different symbols. Both men had written to the other about mathematics, and parts of the *Principia* had been circling among Newton's network of friends, some of whom were also acquaintances of Leibniz. So it is possible that Leibniz had seen Newton's work and rushed to publish it as his own. Newton's celebrity certainly allowed him to paint Leibniz as a plagiarizer. However, most historians now agree that the two men came up with calculus independently and so should both be given equal credit for its invention.

1713

Nicolaus Bernoulli uncovers the St. Petersburg paradox

The Bernoulli (said "ber-noo-lee") family was chock-full of mathematicians. We saw when we looked at Euler's constant, e (see page 22), that it was Jacob Bernoulli who discovered it when looking at money and interest. Euler later joined Jacob's son, Daniel, in St. Petersburg, where he was working on a puzzle set by yet another mathematical member of the Bernoulli family—his cousin Nicolaus. The idea, which Nicolaus first wrote about in a letter to French mathematician Pierre Raymond de Montmort in 1713, ended up being named after the city.

The puzzle revolves around a simple game. A player starts with $2 and tosses a coin. If it comes up heads then her money doubles to $4. The game continues for as long as heads keeps coming up, with the player's money doubling each time that happens. As soon as a tails appears, however, the game ends and she wins the last amount of money offered. So, for example, if she flipped HHHT, she would win $8. You keep that money and start again and you can keep playing the game for as long as you want. The only catch is that you can't play this game for free—you have to pay the casino to enter. How much would you be willing to pay to play Bernoulli's game?

Great expectations

Looking at the game mathematically, you can calculate what's called the "expected value"—how much you could expect to win given all the possibilities. After the first toss, the chances of you winning $2 is ½ (50%). Winning again on the second toss, and getting $4, requires getting two heads in a row, which has a probability of ¼ (½ × ½), and so on.

So the expectation value, E, is equal to (½ × $2) + (¼ × $4) + (⅛ × $8) + (1/16 × $16) + ..., the sequence goes on and on. We can see that E = 1 + 1 + 1 + 1 + ... As the sequence continues forever, E = ∞, thus you should expect to win an infinite amount of money playing this game. So no matter how much money the casino charges to play the game, you should scramble together every last cent

115

you have and bite their hand off. And yet what answer did you give before, when I asked how much money you would be willing to pay? Most people answer with a low amount. That is the St. Petersburg paradox—the disparity between what people are prepared to pay to play and the amount of money they might reasonably expect to win.

Of course, the game assumes that the casino has unlimited resources and will continue to let you play for as long as you want. In reality that would never happen. Yet Bernoulli's game is yet another example that illustrates how our intuition can often let us down.

▲ Nicolaus Bernoulli (1687–1759) was a member of a prolific family of Swiss mathematicians. He first discussed the St. Petersburg Paradox in letters to Pierre Raymond de Montmort.

1,729

The famous taxicab number

Some numbers in mathematics are more famous for the story behind them than for their inherent mathematical power. Perhaps one of the most notorious of these "folklore numbers" is 1,729, otherwise known as the second taxicab number (or Hardy-Ramanujan number).

The story begins with Indian mathematician Srinivasa Ramanujan, who, despite having no formal training, was a mathematical prodigy. When his work came to the attention of the Indian mathematical community, they, in turn, tried to bring it to the attention of scholars in Europe. Initially, his work was rejected or criticized, partly for his lack of formal education. However, one British mathematician, G. H. Hardy, was intrigued by the scrawled equations he had received in the mail. As Hardy himself described them, "They must be true, because, if they were not, no one would have the imagination to invent them."

Hardy wrote to Ramanujan in February 1913 and invited him to Cambridge. Ramanujan initially refused the request due to his Brahmin values. By the following March, he relented and boarded a ship bound for England. The two men had little in common, but for the next five years they would collaborate on many math puzzles. However, England never really suited Ramanujan. The weather was much colder than he was accustomed to and, being a vegetarian, he found it difficult to eat well during the rationing imposed by the outbreak of World War I. He became ill and was sent to convalesce in a home in Putney, London.

▲ During a conversation with Srinivasa Ramanujan (1887–1920, *top*), G. H. Hardy (1877–1947, *bottom*) mentioned the license plate number of a taxicab. Ramanujan noted its special mathematical property.

Upon visiting Ramanujan, perhaps due to their lack of other common ground, Hardy opened the conversation with mathematics. He remarked that he had arrived by taxi and that the cab's number was 1,729. Because this was a seemingly uninteresting number, Hardy said he hoped it wasn't a bad omen. "On the contrary," said Ramanujan, "it is a very interesting number: it is the smallest number expressible as the sum of two cubes in two different ways." That's because $1,729 = 1^3 + 12^3 = 9^3 + 10^3$. Hence a new kind of number passed into mathematical parlance.

Evidence of Ramanujan's exploration of such numbers appears in his notebooks from years before, although there is also evidence they were being considered by mathematicians as early as 1657.

The extent to which this story has become part of the mathematical landscape is illustrated by its use in the popular cartoon *Futurama*. In his book, *The Simpsons and Their Mathematical Secrets* (which also looks at *Futurama*), author Simon Singh reveals just how often the number 1,729 crops up, including as the registry number of a starship called *Nimbus*. In another episode, a character calls for a taxicab and it turns up with the number 87,539,319 on the roof. This is the smallest number that can be written as the sum of two cubes in three different ways ($167^3 + 436^3$, $228^3 + 423^3$ and $255^3 + 414^3$). Hence the cartoon taxicab's number is itself a taxicab number.

1786

William Playfair invents
the line graph and bar chart

When confronted with a sprawling list of numbers, it is often hard to get an intuitive feel for any underlying patterns or trends. In many cases, it is much easier to visualize data in the form of a diagram, with the most common examples being line graphs, bar charts, and pie charts. We have one man to thank for the invention of all three of these widely used ways of representing data: Scottish engineer William Playfair (see box, page 120). In 1786, he published *The Commercial and Political Atlas* containing

Different types of data

Data can be split into two main groups: qualitative and quantitative. Qualitative data are nonnumerical and deal with the description of things. Quantitative data—based on numerical measurements—can be further subdivided into two groups.

Discrete data Data are discrete (sometimes called "discontinuous") if the values they can take are restricted. Shoe size is discrete because you can't be a size 8.72—you have to be an 8½ or a 9. Data that count objects, such as people or record sales, also have to be discrete, because you can't have part of a person or buy half a song.

Continuous data Continuous data can take on any value and are limited only by how accurately your measurements are. Height, weight, temperature, and time are all forms of continuous data. You shouldn't use a bar chart for continuous data—a histogram should be used instead (see main text).

the first line graphs and bar charts, which he used to depict the imports and exports of several countries over time. Then, in 1801, he published the book *Statistical Breviary*, in which he gave the world the pie chart.

It is worth noting that different charts depict different types of data (see box). With that in mind, here's a look at each of Playfair's three diagrams in turn.

Line graphs

These are most often used to depict trends over time. Units of time (be it days, weeks, years, etc.) run along the x-axis and points are placed on the graph to show the value of the variable on the y-axis at that time. Points are joined together by lines, and there is no requirement for lines to join either axis.

It is also possible to combine several graphs into one diagram. This is often the case when it comes to the weather, where climate graphs show both temperature using a line graph and rainfall with a bar graph. This lets you see easily how these two fluctuating variables may or may not be connected.

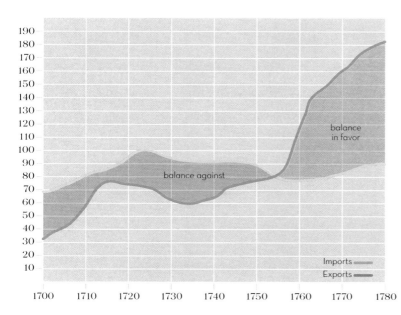

◀ Playfair applied his line graph to depict England's exports and imports (in £10,000s) to and from Denmark and Norway.

Bar charts (and histograms)

Data plotted on a bar graph must be discrete (see top right). The data are divided into categories, which are conventionally placed on the horizontal x-axis. This is why information plotted on bar charts is often called "categorical data." The vertical y-axis shows the number of members belonging to that category (the "frequency"). It could be a group's favorite candies or pets. Adjacent bars should not touch one another. A bar chart can be drawn the other way around with the categories on the y-axis and the frequency on the x-axis. The order in which the bars appear can be freely swapped around and the bars are always the same width.

If the data are continuous, however, then the bar chart's cousin— the histogram—is used (shown bottom right). Here, adjacent bars touch each other to indicate this continuousness. A graph of peak rainfall, for example, would run consecutively day by day—without gaps. While you can reorder the bars in a bar chart, you cannot in a histogram. If the size of the groups is equal, then the bars will all be of equal width. However, because the width of the bar represents the width of the group, it can alter if the groups are different sizes.

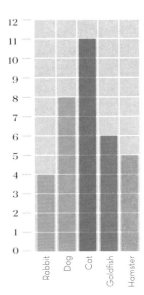

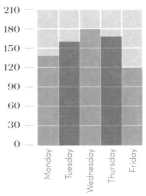

▲ A bar chart (*top*) illustrates discrete/categorical data. The bars do not touch. A histogram (*bottom*)— for example of day-to-day rainfall—shows continuous data and the bars do touch.

William Playfair (1759–1823)

It's fair to say that the inventor of the ubiquitous line graph, bar chart, and pie chart is not a household name. Born in Scotland in 1759, Playfair was an engineer who at one point was personal assistant to James Watt. His father died when William was just 13 years old, leaving his older brother John, another mathematician, to bring him up. By 1787, Playfair had moved to Paris where, like fellow mathematician Galois, he had revolutionary sympathies. He was forced to go back to England due to a libel court case, but returned to France once the monarchy had been restored. He died in Covent Garden, London, on February 11, 1823.

Pie charts

In a pie chart, a circle is divided up into sectors. The size of each sector depicts the proportion of the overall total represented by that particular group.

Say you had collected the following data about the favorite subject of a group of 1,021 pupils at your local school.

Subject	Number of pupils
Math	432
Science	138
English	201
History	133
French	117

▼ Pie charts—invented by William Playfair in 1801—are an easy way to show the contribution that individual categories make to an overall population.

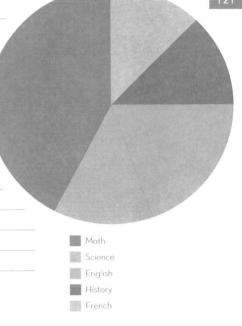

Math
Science
English
History
French

To construct a pie chart from this data, we first have to work out what proportion of a 360° circle should be taken up by each category. With 1,021 pupils, we know that each pupil will be represented by 360/1,021 = 0.353...°. So we can say that each subject should take up the following sized sector:

Subject	Calculation	Size
Math	432 x 0.353° =	152.32°
Science	138 x 0.353° =	48.66°
English	201 x 0.353° =	70.87°
History	133 x 0.353° =	46.90°
French	117 x 0.353° =	41.25°

1822

Charles Babbage proposes
his difference engine

Today, computers are ubiquitous, in daily life and when solving complex mathematical problems. The first computer-generated mathematical proof didn't come until 1976, but machines in mathematics had been proposed more than 150 years earlier. In 1822, British inventor Charles Babbage put forward ideas for an automatic way to calculate the values of polynomic functions.

Charles Babbage (1791–1871)

One of four children, Babbage was born in London to a banking family. Surviving a serious fever as a child, he went on to study mathematics at the University of Cambridge. Within two years of his graduation in 1814 he was elected to the prestigious title of Fellow of the Royal Society (FRS). By 1828, he had become Lucasian Professor of Mathematics at Cambridge (a title once held by Sir Isaac Newton and more recently by Stephen Hawking).

Babbage died of renal inadequacy in 1871, and after his death his brain was preserved. Both halves are in London, one at the Science Museum and the other in the Hunterian.

A polynomic function is an equation that contains several terms added together or subtracted from one another. These terms can include powers (such as squared or cubed) but these "exponents" must be positive (that is, you can have x^2 but you can't have x^{-2}).

For example, $f(x) = x^2 + x + 1$ is a polynomial function—the f stands for function and the (x) just says that its value depends on the value of x. Starting with $x = 1$, you get $f(x) = 3$. For $x = 2$ you get $f(x) = 7$, etc. Creating tables containing the values of polynomic functions in the nineteenth century was done by hand by "human computers." These tables were not error-free, however, the reason why Babbage wanted an automatic way of doing it. Babbage's difference engine consisted of a series of toothed number wheels driven by gears to perform the calculations.

Fledgling funding

His idea was important enough to warrant the British government awarding Babbage £1,500 (more than £180,000 in today's money) to start work on building the machine. However, during Babbage's lifetime, his machine never saw the light of day. Some historians say that was because his design proved beyond the reach of the engineers of the time, others that the failure was due to politics and infighting with lead engineer Joseph Clement. Either way, by the time the project was canned two decades later, more than £17,000 had been shelled out.

During the attempts to build his difference engine, Babbage came up with his ideas for what he called an "analytical engine"—a machine that could be fed a problem using cards with holes punched in them and which had the ability to store information (a memory). It was the first design for a general-purpose computer.

Babbage never managed to see either of his machines built; however, his difference engine was eventually made—by the Science Museum in London in 1991, to celebrate the bicentenary of his birth.

▲ The mathematical machines envisaged by Charles Babbage used a series of toothed wheels to perform calculations, leading to the invention of the first computer.

1837

Poisson publishes
the Poisson distribution

The Poisson distribution, named after a French mathematician (see box opposite), is an area of statistics dealing with the likelihood of events happening if the average rate at which they've occurred previously is already known. It was first published in 1837 as part of *Recherches sur la probabilité des jugements en matière criminelle et en matière civile* (Research on the Probability of Judgments in Criminal and Civil Matters). However, others have noted that fellow Frenchman Abraham de Moivre published a similar result much earlier, in 1711.

Poisson's original motivation was to examine the rate of wrongful criminal convictions. A more colorful application would famously follow in 1898, when Russian economist Ladislaus Bortkiewicz published his book *The Law of Small Numbers*. Its pages show how the number of soliders dying in the Prussian army over a 20-year period as the result of being kicked by a horse followed a Poission distribution.

The Poisson distribution itself is encapsulated in this equation:

$$P(x) = \frac{\mu^x e^{\mu}}{x!}$$

where $P(x)$ is the probability that x number of events will occur in a given time period if they occurred an average of μ times in the past (e is Euler's number, 2.718 ..., and ! is the symbol for factorial).

As always, it pays to give a concrete example. Since its launch in the 1992/93 season, the English Premier League has become the most watched soccer franchise in the world, with around

4.7 billion viewers. Up to the end of the 2014/15 season, English Premier League (EPL) matches have averaged 2.63 goals a game. How probable is it, then, that the next match will be a seven-goal thriller? The Poisson distribution can tell us.

In this case, μ = 2.63 (the average number of goals in previous games) and x = 7 (the number of goals we want to see in the next match). Sticking those numbers into the Poisson distribution formula gives us:

$$P(7) = \frac{2.63^7 e^{-2.63}}{7!} = 0.012 \ldots$$

What that's telling us is that there is roughly a 1% chance of seven goals being scored in the next EPL match. Eager to check this out, I went to a leading betting web site and looked up the odds for the next EPL match to be played (Liverpool vs. Bournemouth). Sure enough, the odds of a 4–3 home win were 100–1.

Siméon-Denis Poisson (1781 – 1840)

A cursory glance at the list of things named after Poisson is enough to illustrate his important contributions to mathematics and the physical sciences. As well as the Poisson distribution, there's the Poisson process, Poisson sampling, Poisson regression, the Poisson bracket, Poisson ratio, and many more besides.

Born the son of a soldier in Pithiviers, France, Poisson studied at the prestigious École Polytechnique in Paris. Within two years he was already publishing important mathematical treatises. When Napoleon sent Joseph Fourier to Grenoble in 1806, Poisson was appointed a professor at the school. He was a celebrated teacher, and it is said he once remarked, "Life is good for only two things: doing mathematics and teaching it."

1847

Boolean algebra is formulated

The modern world is built on 1s and zeros. Inside computer chips, information is stored as an array of zeros and 1s—each known as a binary digit (or bit). There are eight bits to a byte and we now routinely talk in terms of megabytes, gigabytes, and terrabytes.

Just as there is a form of algebra for dealing with conventional numbers, there is a type of algebra used in binary. It is known as Boolean algebra (or Boolean logic) after English mathematician George Boole. In Boolean algebra, 0 and 1 often equate to the statements false and true. There are also three basic operations:

AND (denoted by the symbol ∧ sometimes called "conjunction")
OR   (denoted by the symbol ∨ sometimes called "disjunction")
NOT (denoted by the symbol ¬ sometimes called "negation")

An everyday example shows how it works. Say you decided that you are only going to watch TV if your favorite show is on AND it is raining outside. You could draw the following "truth table":

▲ The work on logic of English mathematician George Boole (1815–64) laid many of the foundations for the digital revolution.

Statement A Your favorite show is on	Statement B It's raining outside	Result You watch TV
True	True	True
False	True	False
True	False	False
False	False	False

You can see, as expected, that you only watch TV if both of your stipulated conditions are met. Instead of writing out TRUE or FALSE every time, you could do the same thing with 0 for FALSE and 1 for TRUE. That would give you:

A	B	R
1	1	1
0	1	0
1	0	0
0	0	0

If your conditions changed so that you'd watch TV if either your favorite show was on OR it was raining outside, the truth table would look different:

A	B	R
1	1	1
0	1	1
1	0	1
0	0	0

These two possibilities can be neatly joined together into a single truth table:

A	B	A∧B	A∨B
1	1	1	1
0	1	0	1
1	0	0	1
0	0	0	0

Similar Boolean calculations are performed inside computers using devices called "logic gates." These gates can be combined in many different ways to let a computer perform a huge range of tasks.

1850

The year the word "matrix" was first used mathematically

In popular culture, the word "matrix" often conjures up images of Neo, epic slow-mo fights, and green numbers falling as digital rain. In math, however, the numbers in a matrix are far more organized.

A matrix (plural matrices) is an array of numbers arranged in a set of rows and columns and is described by the number of those rows and columns—for example, a 2 × 3 matrix. They can be particularly useful when dealing with coordinates. The individual numbers inside matrices are known as "elements." Before James Joseph Sylvester first used the word "matrix" in 1850, these mathematical entities were known as "arrays" and, as for normal numbers or Boolean algebra (see page 126), rules apply to the addition, subtraction, multiplication, and division of matrices.

Two matrices may be added or subtracted only if both contain the same number of rows and columns. If that's the case, you add (or subtract) each element occupying the same spot in each matrix to form a new one. So if we tried to add the 2 × 2 matrix **A** and the 2 × 2 matrix **B**, we can because both have two rows and two columns (matrices are often denoted by a bold capital letter):

$$\mathbf{A} = \begin{bmatrix} 1 & 2 \\ 3 & 4 \end{bmatrix} + \mathbf{B} = \begin{bmatrix} 1 & 3 \\ 5 & 7 \end{bmatrix} = \begin{bmatrix} 2 & 5 \\ 8 & 11 \end{bmatrix} = \mathbf{C}$$

Multiplying matrices is more difficult. It can be done only if the number of columns in the first matrix matches the number of rows in the second. So you can multiply together a 2 × 3 matrix with a 3 × 2 matrix, but not a 2 × 3 by another 2 × 3.

▲ James Joseph Sylvester (1814–1897) was the first to use the term "matrix" for what had previously been known as arrays.

Working out the elements in the resulting matrix requires first calculating something called the "dot product." Take matrices **E** and **F**:

$$E = \begin{bmatrix} 1 & 2 & 3 \\ 4 & 5 & 6 \end{bmatrix} \qquad F = \begin{bmatrix} 7 & 8 \\ 9 & 10 \\ 11 & 12 \end{bmatrix}$$

The dot product of the first row of **E** with the first column of **F** is written $(1, 2, 3) \cdot (7, 9, 11) = 1 \times 7 + 2 \times 9 + 3 \times 11 = 58$. You do the same for **E**'s first row with **F**'s second column. Then **E**'s second row with **F**'s first column before finally **E**'s second row with **F**'s second column. Doing so creates a new matrix, **G**, which is:

$$G = \begin{bmatrix} 58 & 64 \\ 139 & 154 \end{bmatrix}$$

A matrix resulting from a multiplication will always have the same number of rows as the first matrix and the same number of columns as the second.

To divide one matrix by another, you first find something called the inverse matrix and then multiply by that as above. It is the same as dividing by 2 instead of multiplying by the inverse of 2 ($\frac{1}{2}$). The inverse matrix of **A** is written as A^{-1}.

$$\text{If } A = \begin{bmatrix} a & b \\ c & d \end{bmatrix} \text{ then } A^{-1} = \frac{1}{(ad - bc)} \begin{bmatrix} d & -b \\ -c & a \end{bmatrix}$$

So you swap d and a over and put minus signs in front of c and b. The bit outside the brackets is called the "determinant," which you get by multiplying the diagonals of the original matrix, subtracting those answers from each other, and dividing 1 by what you get.

Multiplying a matrix by its inverse results in something called an identity matrix, **I**, which is the same as the number 1 in normal mathematics. In the 2 x 2 case,

$$I = \begin{bmatrix} 1 & 0 \\ 0 & 1 \end{bmatrix}$$

Matrices may seem arcane, but they underpin much of the modern world and are used extensively by engineers, physicists, and even computer games designers.

1858

The Möbius strip is discovered

The Möbius strip—named after August Möbius (see box, opposite)—is perhaps one of the most famous shapes in mathematics. You can make one by taking a strip of paper and creating a loop by turning one end of the paper over by half a turn and gluing it to the other end. This seemingly ordinary shape has some extraordinary properties.

To begin with, it has only one side. Imagine that, before you glued the strip together, you colored in one side of the paper red and the other blue. Once glued, you can traverse the whole shape, passing through red and blue sections, and return to where you started without ever crossing an edge. You would also be upside down compared to where you started. Mathematicians call shapes with this property "nonorientable."

Apart from having only one side, the Möbius strip also has only one edge. Pick any point on the edge of the strip and trace your finger around it and you'll end up where you started.

▼ The Möbius strip is a curious shape with only one side and one edge. You can traverse both blue and red sections of the paper without crossing a boundary.

August Ferdinand Möbius (1790–1868)

A descendant of the famous Protestant reformer Martin Luther, Möbius was born in Schulpforta in Germany. His father, a dance teacher, died when the young Möbius was just three years old. Initially homeschooled until he was 13, he eventually went to study at the University of Leipzig. By 1813, he had moved to the University of Göttingen to work under renowned mathematician and astronomer Carl Friedrich Gauss (see page 70).

Although most famous for the Möbius strip, he actually received his Ph.D. in astronomy, writing a thesis on the occultation of fixed stars. Some historians even doubt Möbius was the first to discover the famous strip. Instead, they say, that honor should go to fellow German mathematician Johann Benedict Listing (1808–1882), who was also the first to coin the mathematical phrase "topology."

Expect the unexpected

Something seemingly perverse happens if you cut the strip in half (down the middle, lengthwise). With an ordinary loop, you would expect to end up with two new loops. After all, you've cut it in half. But with a Möbius strip, you actually end up with a single, larger loop, which now has four half twists in it.

Whether your initial half twist to construct the shape was clockwise or counterclockwise will result in different-looking Möbius strips (albeit with the same general properties). Because these two shapes are not simply mirror images of one another, mathematicians say the shape has "chirality" (the two versions are often said to have "right-handedness" and "left-handedness").

The study of Möbius strips forms part of the mathematical area of topology—the same field kick-started by Euler when he tackled the Bridges of Königsberg problem (see page 40). Like Euler's work, the study of Möbius strips can have real-world applications, too—the B. F. Goodrich Company once patented a conveyor belt with that shape so that each side would be worn evenly and, therefore, the belt would last twice as long.

1880

John Venn formulalizes
his famous diagram

In mathematics, a Venn diagram is a way of depicting the relationship between different groups of things. Mathematicians call these different groups "sets," so Venn diagrams, named after British mathematician John Venn, fall under an area of mathematics known as set theory.

Take the diagram on the opposite page, showing all the numbers from 1 to 10. The first stage of drawing a Venn diagram is to draw a rectangular box, which is known as a "universe" (U). If you want to classify these numbers into two sets—in our case, even numbers and prime numbers—you draw two circles and fill those

John Venn (1834–1923)

Born to a long line of clergymen, Venn had a strict upbringing. After studying mathematics at Cambridge, he too became a priest. He later returned to Cambridge, and it was during his time there that he hit upon his idea of representing sets in the form of a simple diagram. He said of his brainwave: "Of course the device was not new then, but it was so obviously representative of the way in which anyone who approached the subject from the mathematical side would attempt to visualize propositions, that it was forced upon me almost at once." It wasn't new because Venn diagrams are similar to Euler diagrams, which had been invented by Leonhard Euler a century earlier. In fact, Venn himself called his diagrams "Eulerian Circles."

circles with the appropriate numbers. Because there is one number between 1 and 10 that is both even and prime—2—the circles overlap and 2 is placed in that overlapping area. Any number that doesn't fall into either set sits outside the circles but inside the universe (the box).

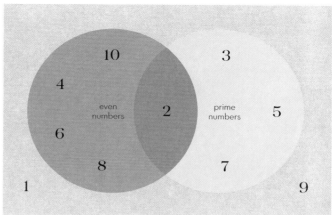

Mathematicans have particular names and notations for representing which part of the universe they are referring to:

▲ A Venn diagram showing the numbers 1-9 arranged into two sets: odd numbers and prime numbers. Those that are neither even nor prime sit outside the circles.

THE INTERSECTION This is the area where two sets, set A and set B, overlap, often written A ∩ B. There's only one number between 1 and 10 that's even AND prime.

THE UNION All items that lie inside either set A or set B, written A ∪ B. In our case, that's any number between 1 and 10 that's either even OR prime.

THE SYMMETRIC DIFFERENCE Anything belonging to either set but not to both—that is, items located in the intersection don't count. This is written A △ B.

THE (ABSOLUTE) COMPLEMENT The complement of a set refers to all the elements contained within the universe that do not belong to that set. So the complement of set A (our even numbers) would be any number from 1 to 10 that isn't even, irrespective of whether it is prime or not. The complement is often denoted Aᶜ (or sometimes A' or A).

THE RELATIVE COMPLEMENT This is the part of a set not including any elements in intersections. "The relative complement of A in B" would be all the prime numbers with any even primes removed—that is, 3, 5, and 7. The relative complement is written variously as B − A or B\A.

1882

The Klein bottle is invented

Just like the Möbius strip, the Klein bottle is a nonorientable surface (see page 130). Perhaps "bottle" is an unfortunate term for it—bottles tend to be able to hold liquids, but the strange properties of the Klein bottle mean that any liquid you put in would just come back out again.

To create one, first take a rectangular sheet of material and mark its two pairs of edges (see the diagrams). Then fold the two

Felix Klein (1849–1925)

Born in Düsseldorf, Germany, Felix Klein was a key player in late nineteenth-century mathematics. His research included work on group theory (see page 53) and complex numbers (see page 103) However, he originally intended to be a physicist, studying both physics and math at the University of Bonn. For a short time, he served in the Prussian army, before being made a professor at the young age of 23. Later in his career, he set up a mathematics center at the University of Göttingen and recruited fellow German mathematician David Hilbert (see page 54) to join him. Klein also played an important role in determining the mathematical curriculum for schools.

▲ Making a Klein bottle involves joining two ends of a cylinder so that they have matching orientations. This is impossible in three dimensions without puncturing the bottle.

long edges together to form a cylinder. Bring the two ends of the cylinder together and you'll notice they don't share the same orientation (one arrow goes clockwise and the other counterclockwise). The only way to match their orientation is to pass one end through the cylinder itself and attach it to the other end. However, there's a catch. In topology, two shapes are equivalent only if they have the same number of holes. By punching a hole in the cylinder to pass one end through, you have made a topologically different shape.

This means that a Klein bottle is impossible in our three-dimensional world. In a hypothetical four-dimensional world, however, you could use the extra dimension to pass the end around the cylinder and join the other end without a hole. Three-dimensional approximations to the Klein bottle made using a hole are called punctured Klein bottles.

No edges, one side

In some ways, Klein's bottle is similar to a sphere—both have "closed" surfaces. Take our Earth as an example. If you walk out from your front door and keep traveling in a straight line over land and sea, you will end up back where you started. You can do this over and over again without limit. Similarly, an ant crawling around the surface of a Klein bottle would never find a boundary or an edge. However, a sphere has two sides (an inside and an outside), whereas the Klein bottle only has one. Imagine a basketball. To get from a point on the outside of the ball to a point on the inside, you have to cross a boundary. Yet an ant crawling around a Klein bottle would have access to both sides of any given point on its surface without having to cross a boundary— it's all just one big side. This means it cannot enclose a volume, and so it would never be able to hold a liquid.

▼ A three-dimensional approximation of a Klein bottle known as a punctured Klein bottle. It can hold a liquid, whereas a true Klein bottle cannot.

1936

First Fields Medal awarded

In the 1997 Oscar-winning movie *Good Will Hunting*, the title character (played by Matt Damon) is a mathematical prodigy from the wrong side of the tracks who comes to the attention of Professor Gerald Lambeau after he solves a mathematical puzzle left on a university blackboard. In the movie, we are told that Lambeau is a Fields Medal winner and yet Will can solve problems he cannot. Another character, Sean (played by the late Robin Williams), declares: "The Fields Medal, it's a really big deal."

The Fields Medal is often referred to as "the Nobel Prize for mathematicians." There isn't a Nobel Prize for mathematics (although there is one for economic sciences). Unlike the Nobels, which are awarded every year, the Fields Medal is only handed out every four years to either two, three, or four mathematicians. In an attempt to encourage young researchers, all winners must be under 40 years old.

▼ The Fields Medal, funded and designed by Canadian mathematician John Charles Fields, is awarded every four years to a mathematician under the age of 40.

John Charles Fields (1863–1932)

Born in Hamilton, Ontario, Canada, Fields graduated from the University of Toronto in 1884 before moving to the United States to complete his doctorate. By 1891, he had made the decision to leave North America for Europe and set himself up in France and Germany. While there, he rubbed shoulders with some of the mathematical luminaries of the age, including Felix Klein (see page 134).

Returning to Canada in 1902, he steadily tried to raise the profile of mathematics both in academic circles and in wider public consciousness. As part of these efforts, he planned what would go on to become the Fields Medal. He died four years before the first award was made, but he left C$47,000 in his will to fund the prize—a substantial amount of money in 1932. He is buried in Hamilton Cemetery.

It is awarded by the International Congress of the International Mathematical Union (IMU) and currently comes with a prize of C$15,000—Canadian dollars due to the fact that it was set up by Canadian mathematician John Fields (see box, above). Fields not only stumped up the prize money, he also designed the medal. A similar award, the Abel Prize (named after Niels Abel), was established by the Norwegian government in 2002 and comes with a prize of six million Norwegian krone (around $750,000) .

The first Fields Medal was awarded in 1936 at a ceremony in Oslo, Norway, to Finn Lars Ahlfors and American Jesse Douglas. The next prize ceremony took place in 1950 (in Cambridge, Massachusetts) and since then has been conducted every four years. However, it was 2014 before a woman was recognized with the prize—Iranian Maryam Mirzakhani, for her work on the dynamics and geometry of Riemann surfaces. Other notable winners include Jean-Pierre Serre in 1954—the youngest ever recipient at just 27—for work involving spheres. In 2006, Russian mathematician Grigori Perelman declined the Fields medal for his work on the Poincaré conjecture. He also declined the Clay Institute's Millennium Prize (see page 153).

1995

Proof of Fermat's last theorem announced

Of all the theorems in this book, the question behind what became known as Fermat's last theorem has to be one of the easiest to ask and the most difficult to answer. We saw earlier how Pythagoras worked out that the lengths of the sides of a right triangle are related by the formula $a^2 + b^2 = c^2$ (see page 15). And there are many values for a and b for which this holds (in fact, there is an infinite number of them).

What French mathematician Pierre de Fermat began wondering in the seventeenth century is whether the same relationship holds if you increase the exponent to a number higher than 2; that is, could you find values for a and b such that $a^3 + b^3 = c^3$ or $a^4 + b^4 = c^4$, etc. He couldn't find any. But he didn't just give up—instead, he argued that the reason he couldn't find any was that there weren't any. Around 1637, he even went as far as to scribble in the margin of a book that he had proof but there wasn't enough room in the margin to write it down. This is all the more impressive given that he was actually a lawyer who was only moonlighting with mathematics in the evening. After Fermat's death almost 30 years later, his son discovered many other allusions to mathematical secrets strewn throughout the same book—*Arithmetica* by Diophantus.

Fermat's son would go on to publish a new version of the book, complete with his father's additions. Over the decades and centuries that followed, successive generations of mathematicians were able to show that all but one of Fermat's ideas held water.

The only proof that remained elusive was the one relating to the Pythagorean equation with exponents greater than 2. For this reason, it became known as Fermat's last theorem.

Searching for a solution

Mathematicians did make some early headway. It seems that Fermat himself definitely proved that it was impossible when the exponent is equal to 4. By the mid-nineteenth century, it had been shown that exponents of 3, 5, and 7 don't work either. Then, eventually, mathematicians were able to show that Fermat was right for any prime number exponent up to four million.

It would take until 1995 for a complete proof for all exponents to be formally published by English mathematician Andrew Wiles. He has since said he first encountered Fermat's last theorem at the age of 10 after reading about it at his local library. Even then, the young Wiles was determined to prove it. However, soon realizing how difficult it was, he abandoned the idea, only to pick it up again in his thirties. He then spent the next six years religiously working on the problem, often in secrecy. In September 1994, almost at the point of giving up the task for good, Wiles solved the final piece of the puzzle that would see him prove the theorem once and for all. That work saw him knighted in 2000 by Queen Elizabeth II.

▲ Andrew Wiles (b. 1953) next to a statue of Pierre de Fermat. In 1995, he published proof of the theorem etched in the stone.

2006

The Gömböc problem is solved

Do you remember the Weeble toys from your childhood? They're the slightly sinister egg-shape people who, when knocked down, would always manage to get back up again. The secret to their ability to rouse themselves is the way they are cleverly weighted so that gravity always pulls them back into place.

But what about a shape that rights itself without any biased weighting, one that's made of the same material all the way through? That was the challenge set by Russian mathematician Vladimir Arnold in 1995 when he suggested such a shape might exist. In the language of mathematicians, such a shape would have only one stable point of equilibrium—ways you can place the shape on a flat surface and it will balance forever. Such a shape would always return to this stable point, no matter how you placed it on a table—it would always right itself.

The shape was eventually discovered by two Hungarian scientists, Gábor Domokos and Péter Várkonyi, in 2006. As part of their attempts to find the right shape, Domokos and his wife trawled a Greek beach on their vacation and tested more than 2,000 pebbles to see whether they behaved in such a way. They didn't, and he had to go back to the drawing board. The gömböc shape has to be made to within 0.1% in order to work.

▼ The evenly weighed gömböc shape will always right itself. However, it has to be constructed to within 0.1% to work.

3,435
The only Münchhausen number

In *Münchhausen*, a 1943 German movie, the character Baron Hieronymus von Münchhausen raises himself into the air by riding a cannonball all the way to a Turkish palace, where he is later enslaved. Or, at least, that's what he claims—he was well known for telling outrageous tales about himself. Münchhausen numbers get their name from this fictitious baron, because they, too, are particularly self-obsessed.

Discounting the number 1, there is only one true Münchhausen number: 3,435. This is because $3^3 + 4^4 + 3^3 + 5^5 = 3,435$. Every digit, raised to the power of itself and added together, conjures up the original number. Obviously $1^1 = 1$ is a trivial and fairly uninteresting example—you're not splitting the number up.

It is sometimes argued that there are actually four Münchhausen numbers: 0, 1, 3,435, and 438,579,088. However, the first and last numbers in that list rely on calculating 0^0 and getting the answer 0. Normally, raising something to the power of zero will always equal 1 anyway. Yet in this case, 0^0 is what mathematicians call "undefined"—it doesn't have an answer. Try sticking it into a calculator and the machine will not return a zero but an error instead (just like 0/0, see page 11).

So, the only true Münchhausen number—the only multiple-digit number you can split up into its constituent digits, raise each one to the power of itself, and add them together to return your original number—is 3,435.

▲ The fictional character Baron Hieronymus von Münchhausen lends his name to a type of number that is as obsessed with itself as he was.

5,050

The sum of the numbers 1 to 100

Carl Friedrich Gauss (1777-1855) is one of the most revered mathematicians in history. He was a prodigious mathematical talent even from an early age. One particular story from his childhood days has passed into mathematical folklore.

It is said that when he was 10 years old, his teacher set the class a problem. He asked them to add up all the numbers from 1 to 100 and bring their answers up to the front of the class once they'd finished. To the teacher's surprise, Gauss quickly sprang toward the teacher with the number 5,050 while the rest of the class were still busy totting up the numbers.

Gauss's answer was indeed correct and he was able to be so speedy because he noticed a much quicker way to work it out than simply adding up all the numbers. His insight was that every one of the numbers from 1 to 100 can be paired up with another to make 101 (100 + 1, 99 + 2, 98 + 3, and so on). He could see that there were 50 such pairs and so he simply did 101 × 50 to swiftly reach the correct answer of 5,050.

Gauss would grow up to revolutionize mathematics, but perhaps he took his work a little too seriously. It is said that upon being told his wife was dying, he remarked, "Ask her to wait a moment—I am almost done."

▼ The story of Carl Friedrich Gauss and his prodigious childhood is a famous one. It is uncertain whether it is true, but it's certainly a good tale.

6,174

Kaprekar's constant

In 1949, Indian mathematician and schoolteacher D. R. Kaprekar (1905-1986) discovered a curious quirk of the number 6,174, which is now named after him. He realized that if you take any four-digit number, as long as none of the four digits are the same, and apply a particular procedure to them, you always arrive at the number 6,174.

Here's Kaprekar's procedure. First, you take the four-digit number and rearrange the digits in order of largest to smallest. You then arrange them from smallest to largest. Subtract the second number from the first. You then give the same treatment to this new number. Eventually, you will end up with 6,174, and it will never take more than seven times or "iterations."

Let's test it out with 4,793. Rearranging from highest to lowest gives 9,743, and from lowest to highest gives 3,479. Subtract the two and you get 6,264. Rearrange this number in the same way and you get 6,642 – 2,466 = 4,176. One more try leads to 7,641 – 1,467 = 6,174. This always works, as long as all four numbers aren't the same. You can even have trailing zeroes in your original number (such as 0791). If you keep repeating the process once you reach 6,174 you just get stuck because 7,614 – 1,467 = 6,174.

If you carry out the same procedure with three-digit numbers, the answer always converges on 495.

14,316

First in a chain of
28 sociable numbers

An extension of perfect and amicable numbers (see page 38 and page 86), sociable numbers are also based on the numbers that divide into them. A group of numbers is considered sociable if by summing the divisors of one number, you reach another number, and by continually repeating this process you eventually arrive back at the original number. They were discovered and named in 1918 by the Belgian mathematician Paul Poulet.

Take the example of 1,264,460. If you sum up all the numbers that divide into it, you get 1,547,860. Sum up its divisors and you get 1,727,636. Repeat the process and you end up with 1,305,184. Do it one last time and you end up back at 1,264,460.

These numbers are said to form a chain of sociable numbers. Notice that if the chain has just one "link"—that is, a single number's divisors sum up to itself—that's the same as a perfect number. If the chain has two links—that is, the divisors of two numbers sum up to the other number—that's the same as an amicable number. There are no sociable chains that contain three links, but 225 such as the example above, that contain four.

Amazingly, there is one sociable chain that contains 28 links. It begins (and ends) with the number 14,316.

17,152

Solutions to the
Stomachion puzzle

The Stomachion puzzle comprises a square that has been cut up into 14 pieces, and one way to play a game with them is to try to arrange them in such a way that you re-form the square. The mathematical properties of the puzzle are thought to have been first studied by ancient Greek mathematician Archimedes.

We are lucky to know of Archimedes's work on the puzzle at all. All that survived was a tenth-century copy of his original writing, which was then written over in the thirteenth century with religious text. Work between 1998 and 2008 to retrieve the original manuscript has enabled scholars to decipher what was initially written.

In total, there are 17,152 unique ways that you can configure the shapes to make a square, but in 2003 American mathematician Bill Cutler showed that only 536 of them are not rotations or reflections of any of the others. All 17,152 solutions have an interesting property. First, divide the square up into a 12 × 12 grid of smaller squares. Once you find one solution to the puzzle, mark the positions of the corners of each piece on the grid. The other 17,151 solutions will also have the corners of the pieces falling on these same 16 points.

There are also three pairs of tiles that must always be placed alongside each other for a solution to be found (see the diagram).

▼ The 14-piece Stomachion is one of the oldest mathematical puzzles still known to exist. It has 536 unique solutions.

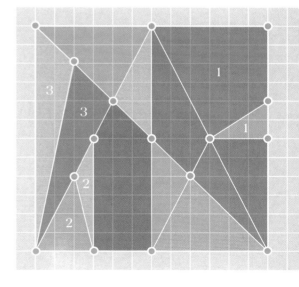

20,000 BCE

Oldest evidence of humans' appreciation of prime numbers

An incredible artifact sits on display in the Royal Belgian Institute of Natural Sciences in Brussels—the fibula bone of a baboon. It was discovered in 1960 in the Ishango region of what is now the Democratic Republic of the Congo and is thought to be more than 20,000 years old. At that time, a community of early humans had settled around the nearby Semliki River, using it for fishing and water. They would later be buried during a devastating volcanic eruption.

What's remarkable about this dark brown bone is that our ancestors had clearly etched notches into it, arranged into three columns. The left-hand column contains marks representing all the prime numbers between 10 and 20 (11, 13, 17, and 19). It is the second oldest mathematical object known to exist (the oldest is the 35,000 year old Lebombo bone with 29 notches, probably used to track the phases of the Moon).

However, there has been heated debate among mathematical historians over whether this is just a coincidence, or whether the people of Ishango appreciated the special properties of those numbers. This is because in order to realize a number is prime, you must first understand the concept of division. Some commentators believe this didn't develop until 10,000 BCE, meaning that while the bone does indeed depict prime numbers, their inscriber might not have appreciated them for the important numbers they are.

▲ The Ishango bone is on display in the Royal Belgian Institute of Natural Sciences in Brussels. Marks depicting prime numbers were etched into the bone more than 20,000 years ago.

30,940

(to one) Odds of a royal flush in Texas Hold'em poker

In the card game poker, hands are ranked in terms of the probability of getting them. In one of the most popular forms of the game, known as Texas Hold'em, a player's best hand is made from five out of the seven cards in play. The top-ranking hand is a "royal flush"—10, jack, queen, king, and ace all of the same suit.

To calculate the odds of hitting a royal flush, we need to find the total number of ways it is possible to get a royal flush and divide that by the total number of different hands possible with seven cards.

In probability theory, the formula for randomly choosing a subset from a larger set is written as:

$$\binom{n}{r} = \frac{n!}{r!(n-r)!}$$

In our case, n is the total number of cards available at the start of the game (52) and r is the number of cards from which you can make your best five-card hand (7). This is said "52 choose 7." As previously, the ! symbol means factorial (see page 95).

Plugging those numbers into a calculator gives you 133,784,560 possible seven-card combinations with a 52-card deck. If you've hit a royal flush, it doesn't matter what the other two cards are—they can be any of the 47 other cards. This is "47 choose 2," which equals 4,324. So there are 4,324 seven-card combinations that will contain a five-card royal flush. The odds of hitting a royal flush are, therefore, 4,324/133,784,560 or 0.000032 or, equivalently, 0.0032% or 30,940 to 1.

▲ A royal flush is 10, jack, queen, king, and ace, all of the same suit. It is the best hand because it is the least likely to occur.

44,488

First in a sequence of five
consecutive happy numbers

As well as being sociable, amicable, weird, abundant, vampiric, or narcissistic, numbers can also be classified as happy or sad.

To find out the "mood" of a number, square its individual digits, then add the answers together. Keep doing this and eventually you'll end up reaching 1 or getting stuck in a loop. Numbers that result in loops are "unhappy," those resulting in 1 (a neat ending) are happy.

This means, then, that 28 is happy. That's because $2^2 + 8^2 = 68$, then $6^2 + 8^2 = 100$, and finally $1^2 + 0^2 + 0^2 = 1$. There are 143 happy numbers below 1,000 and 23 happy numbers below 500 that are also prime.

If you look at higher numbers, you'll come across five happy numbers one after the other: 44,488, 44,489, 44,490, 44,491, and 44,492. The number of happy numbers is actually infinite, with the highest known happy prime number also a Mersenne prime ($2^{42643801} - 1$).

In an episode of the British sci-fi TV show *Doctor Who* called "42," a string of four happy prime numbers (313, 331, 367, and 379) is used as the code to the door of a spaceship that is on a collision course with a star. The Doctor, realizing none of his companions know what a happy number is, retorts, "Don't they teach recreational mathematics anymore?"

65,537

Number of sides of a 65,537-gon

We've seen in earlier chapters that a polygon is a flat, two-dimensional shape (see page 36). A polygon is said to be "constructible" if it can be drawn with a pair of compasses and a straightedge (which is like a ruler). For example, triangles, squares, and pentagons are constructible, but heptagons (seven sides) and nonagons (nine sides) are not.

Why? And what about polygons with even higher numbers of sides? German mathematician Carl Friedrich Gauss (see page 70) was fascinated with this area and set out to find the answers. In 1796, he showed that a polygon with 17 sides was constructible. By 1801, he thought he had come up with a rule to determine whether any n-side polygon is constructible or not. However, it wasn't until 1837 that his idea was proven by French mathematician Pierre Wantzel. For this reason, the result is known as the Gauss-Wantzel theorem. It says that a polygon is constructible if the number of sides it has is equal to a power of 2 multiplied by any number of distinct Fermat primes (including none).

There are currently only five Fermat primes (see page 96) known to exist: 3, 5, 17, 257, and 65,537. So Gauss's 17-side shape is constructible as $17 = 2^0 \times 17$. Similarly, a 65,537-side shape (called a 65,537-gon) is constructible as $65,537 = 2^0 \times 65,537$. This shape has so many sides that you couldn't tell it apart from a circle—it differs by only 15 parts in a billion.

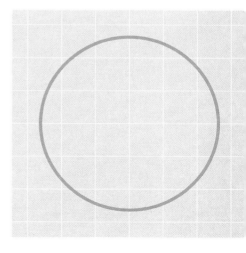

▼ According to the Gauss-Wantzel theorem, the 65,537-gon is constructible with a pair of compasses and a straight-edge. It is barely distinguishable from a circle.

85,900

Destinations included in 2006 solution to a Traveling Salesman problem

Increasingly in the modern world, time is money. The quicker you can do something, the more chance you have to earn more. This is especially true when it comes to delivering packages—the quicker you can drop off each package, the more packages you can deliver in a day and the more profit you stand to make.

The shrewd delivery worker (or their employer) looks for the optimal route for their delivery route, the path taking them to all the places they need to go (including returning home at the end) while covering the shortest overall distance. Finding such a route is known in mathematics as a "Traveling Salesman problem" (TSP), the idea being that door-to-door salesmen face similar pressures as delivery workers. The original question was posed as far back as the nineteenth century when it was referred to as the "messenger problem," before it was given its now widely used name by American mathematician Hassler Whitney in the 1930s.

It is an example of an "optimization" problem—it is asking what is the optimal route. Your first angle of attack might be the so-called "brute force" approach. You work out all possible routes and simply choose the quickest. However, this is far harder than it appears. Imagine you're a delivery driver; you have just ten deliveries to make in a day and you want to find the shortest route between your drops. The total number of different routes you could take in order to visit all ten places is equal to (10-1)! (9 factorial) or 362,880. Even if you could check one route per second, it would take you around 100 hours to establish the optimum route.

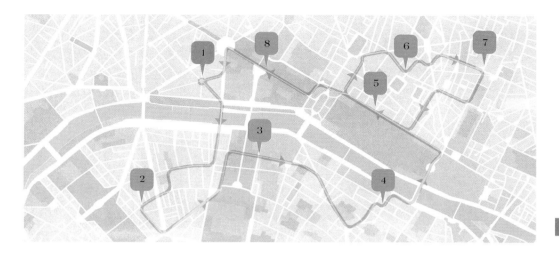

Beating brute force

An improvement to the brute-force approach is the Held-Karp algorithm, which is able to solve the problem for n destinations in $n^2 2^n$ steps. So for ten drops, that's $10^2 \times 2^{10} = 100 \times 1{,}024 = 102{,}400$ steps—a greater than threefold increase on brute force alone.

However, there is no mathematical solution to the problem. No formula can give you the optimal route. It is what mathematicians refer to as an NP-hard problem and a solution to a related puzzle forms part of the $1,000,000 Millennium prizes offered by the Clay Mathematics Institute (see page 153).

Given the fiendishness of the problem, it isn't always necessary to find the optimal route. Finding a path in the top 5 or 10% of shortest routes will often suffice, particularly because the expense of getting enough computer power to solve the problem will probably mitigate any efficiency savings made from an improved route. Nowadays, computer algorithms can find solutions to TSPs between millions of stops that lie within a few percent of the best possible answer. The record for the most number of stops for which the best possible answer has been found is 85,900, set in 2006 by a team led by American mathematician William Cook.

▲ Mathematics can offer a better solution to a Traveling Salesman problem than brute force alone, but currently cannot provide a way to find the optimum solution.

142,857

The basis of cyclic numbers

The only cyclic number that does not start with a zero is 142,857. To see why 142,857 is cyclic, multiply it by any number that is not a multiple of 7 and then add the last six digits of that number to the rest. What you'll get back is a number than contains all six digits of 142,857.

Let's take a couple of examples, trying 101 first. 142,857 × 101 = 14,428,557. We now take the last six digits of that number (428,557) and add them to what's left at the front (14) to get 428,571, which can be rearranged to make 142,857.

You might say I picked 101 for some special reason, so let's try another number: 2,531. 142,857 × 2,531 = 361,571,067. Take the last six digits (571,067) and add that to what's left (361) and you get 571,428 which again you can rearrange to get 142,857.

To see why this works (and also why using a multiple of 7 does not work), let's take a look at the fraction 1/7. It is equal to 0.142857142857142857... Our cyclic number just repeats after the decimal point. By performing the procedure above, you're shifting the decimal point around but you'll always have a bank of six numbers containing those six digits in some order. Multiplying by a multiple of 7, however, will leave you with the answer 999,999.

1,000,000

Dollars turned down by Grigori Perelman for solving Poincaré conjecture

Just as David Hilbert reflected on the state of mathematics at the turn of the twentieth century (see page 54), modern mathematicians undertook a similar exercise at the turn of the twenty-first. But arguably this time the stakes were much higher. In 2000, the Clay Mathematics Institute, based in Cambridge, Massachusetts, offered $1,000,000 "Millennium Prizes" for the solution to each of seven outstanding mathematical problems. Only one of the seven (the Riemann hypothesis) also appeared on Hilbert's list from a century earlier.

Since then, only one of the problems—the Poincaré conjecture—has been solved. However, reclusive Russian mathematician Grigori Perelman (see box, page 154) turned down the financial reward in 2010, arguing that it was unfair to recognize him over other mathematicians who had also made a significant contribution to the problem. He had earlier also rejected the prestigious Fields Medal (see page 137), declaring: "I'm not interested in money or fame; I don't want to be on display like an animal in a zoo."

▼ Henri Poincaré (1854–1912) conjectured in 1904 that any four-dimensional shape without holes is homomorphic to a four-dimensional sphere.

The conjecture he had proved concerns spheres. In 1904, French mathematician Henri Poincaré made a suggestion based on his work on topology. Mathematicians say that two shapes are topologically equivalent (or "homeomorphic") if one can be transformed into the other without changing the number of holes it contains or cutting the shape and sticking parts of it back together. So, a square and a triangle are homeomorphic, because you can squash (a "continuous deformation") the sides of the square to form a triangle. However, a sphere and a doughnut shape (known mathematically as a "torus") are not homeomorphic, because once you've flattened the sphere you have to punch a hole in the middle. Topologists are able to extend this study of shapes beyond three dimensions, too. Poincaré's conjecture states that any four-dimensional shape without holes is homeomorphic to a four-dimensional sphere.

Along with proof of Fermat's last theorem (see page 138), proof of the Poincaré conjecture is among the greatest achievements in recent mathematical history. However, arguably an even greater

Grigori Perelman (b. 1966)

In 2003, at the age of just 37, Grigori Perelman's work on the Poincaré conjecture set the mathematical world alight. Mathematicians pored over his work for months, analyzing every line and equation. Satisfied that he had indeed made the elusive breakthrough, they threw every accolade at him, from the Fields Medal to a Millennium Prize. He turned them all down.

He was born in what is now St. Petersburg and his mother gave up her own studies in mathematics to stay at home with young Grigori. When he later withdrew from the mathematical limelight after his discovery, it is believed he moved back in with his mother in his hometown. It is not known if he is still working on mathematics.

triumph would be to prove the problem that appears on both the Hilbert and Clay Institute lists—the Riemann hypothesis.

Probing the primes

The Riemann hypothesis, named after German mathematician Bernhard Riemann, concerns the distribution of prime numbers. We've seen several times throughout this book that mathematicians have attempted to conjure up an equation that gives you all the prime numbers. In part, they've been successful—ideas such as Mills' constant (see page 14) and Fermat's conjecture (see page 96) have been able to reproduce parts of the list.

▲ Bernhard Riemann (1826–1866) thought he had found the secret to how prime numbers are distributed. However, his hypothesis remains unproven.

By 1859, Riemann was investigating an area of mathematics known as the "zeta function." A function is just a mathematical machine for turning one number into another. An example of a non-zeta function would be $x^2 + 1$, which turns 1 into 2 and 2 into 5, etc. Riemann noticed something interesting about the inputs that the zeta function turned into zero. When he plotted them on a graph, they all appeared on the same straight line—a telltale sign there may be something deeper going on. Riemann was also able to see a connection between these zero-giving inputs and the prime numbers. So, he reasoned, if there was an order to the inputs, maybe there was a hidden order to the primes, too. The Riemann hypothesis is, therefore, that every possible input to the zeta function that ends up being turned into a zero also appears on that straight line (except for a few exceptions he was already aware of).

Modern computers have helped in part—they have found billions of inputs that the zeta function turns into zeroes and they do all lie on that same straight line. However, that is not proof that one exists that doesn't.

4,937,775

The original Smith number

Mathematicians can sometimes take inspiration from the unlikeliest places. Just as Ramanujan and Hardy took inspiration from taxicabs (see page 116), American mathematician Albert Wilansky gained his insight from a telephone book.

Wilansky was trying to get in contact with his brother-in-law, Harold Smith. Not having his phone number on hand, Wilansky looked it up in the telephone book and noted down that it was 493-7775. He later realized that this number had a special property: if you break the number down into its prime factors and then add them up, they sum up to the same as the individual digits of the number added together.

While Harold Smith's phone number was the first Smith number Wilanksy found, there are smaller ones. To see how they work, it pays to start with one of these smaller numbers. Let's take 58, which written as a multiplication of its prime factors is 2×29. It is a Smith number, because $5 + 8 = 2 + 2 + 9 = 13$. Similarly, 265 is a Smith number, because it can be written using prime numbers as 5×53 and $2 + 6 + 5 = 5 + 5 + 3 = 13$.

For Smith's original telephone number, its prime factors are: $3 \times 5 \times 5 \times 65{,}837$ and $4 + 9 + 3 + 7 + 7 + 7 + 5 = 3 + 5 + 5 + 6 + 5 + 8 + 3 + 7 = 42$.

381,654,729

A pan-digital number where
first n digits are divisible by n

This number has some really interesting properties. For example, it is pan-digital—it is a nine-digit number made up of every number from 1 to 9 used exactly once. But a closer inspection reveals an even more curious property.

Start from the front and begin breaking the number up into chunks. Each chunk can be exactly divided by the number of numbers in that chunk.

So take the first number, 3—it is divisible by 1. The first two numbers together, 38, are divisible by 2. And the pattern continues. See the table for all the stages.

This is almost certainly the most interesting pan-digital number; however, there are a lot to choose from. The total number of nine-digit pan-digital numbers is equal to the total number of different ways you can arrange nine objects in unique orders. That is equal to 9! = 9 × 8 × 7 × 6 × 5 × 4 × 3 × 2 × 1 = 362,880.

Chunk	Number of digits in chunk	Chunk/Number of digits
3	1	3
38	2	19
381	3	127
3,816	4	954
38,165	5	7,633
38,1654	6	63,609
3,816,547	7	545,221
38,165,472	8	4,770,684
381,654,729	9	42,406,081

18,446,744,073,709,551,615

Number of grains of rice in chessboard problem

The rice and chessboard problem is an ancient one. The earliest record of it dates back to a Persian poem written more than a thousand years ago by Firdawsi (935–1025). The story goes something like this.

In an ancient kingdom, a generous and fair king has just passed away. During his reign, he was never flashy with money and not a fan of ostentation. The same could not be said of the new king, his son, who would throw his newfound wealth around as if it knew no bounds. The old king's most trusted advisor, horrified by the reckless abandon of the throne's latest incumbent, set his mind on teaching the newcomer a lesson.

The day before, the new king had devised a competition for which the prize was anything the victor desired. The advisor, being wise and cunning, won the competition and claimed his prize. All he asked for was a chessboard on which a single grain of rice was to be placed on the first square. The only catch was that every day the king must fill up the next square with double the amount of rice from the previous day. Two grains on the second square, four on the third, etc.

▼ The amount of rice needed on each square to complete the task. The letters denote powers of ten: K = thousand, M = million, G = billion, T = trillion, P = quadrillion, and E = quintillion.

							128
256	512	1024	2048	4096	8192	16384	32768
66536	131K	262K	524K	1M	2M	4M	8M
16M	33M	67M	134M	268M	536M	1G	2G
4G	8G	17G	34G	68G	137G	274G	549G
1T	2T	4T	8T	17T	25T	70T	140T
281T	562T	1P	2P	4P	9P	18P	36P
72P	144P	288P	576P	1E	2E	4E	9E

Astounded by the advisor's seemingly trivial request, the young, inexperienced king readily agreed. He was foolish. By the 64th day, the king owed his father's favorite a staggering 18,446,744,073,709,551,615 grains of rice—enough to form a pile larger than Mount Everest and a thousand times more rice than we produce every year in modern times. It is a lesson in trusting your intuition over mathematical rigor. Had the new king been well versed in geometrical progressions, he would have seen through the advisor's scheme.

The power of math

The sequence that can calculate the total number of rice grains, T, begins:

$T = 1 + 2 + 4 + 8 + 16 + ...$

This is called a geometric sequence because there is a fixed ratio between successive terms (in this case, 2). An arithmetic sequence would have its terms go up by a fixed amount each time, such as $1 + 2 + 3 + 4 + 5 + ...$ (a common difference of one between terms).

We can also write our geometric sequence for the rice grains in terms of powers of 2:

$T = 2^0 + 2^1 + 2^2 + 2^3 + 2^4 + ...$

Instead of writing out all the steps, mathematicians have a shorthand for such sequences, called "capital-sigma notation" (sigma is a letter of the Greek alphabet). So it becomes:

$$\sum_{i=0}^{63} 2^i$$

The capital sigma means add up all the terms and the terms themselves are represented by the 2^i. The instruction below the sigma tells you to start with $i = 0$ and you keep going, successively replacing i with every number up to and including the number above the sigma (in this case 63, because there are 64 squares on the board and we started at 0 to make sure the first term was equal to 1).

357,686,312,646,216,567,629,137

Largest truncatable
prime number

A truncatable prime is any prime number that continues to spawn new prime numbers when you start removing numbers from either the beginning or the end (always from the same end in any given instance). The only caveat is that the original number cannot contain a zero. Numbers that exhibit this behavior when you start from the beginning are called "left-truncatable primes" and those that work when you start cutting from the end are called "right-truncatable primes."

Take, for example, the prime number 2,339. Remove the last digit and you get 233, which is also prime. Do it again and you get 23, which is still prime. One more time leaves you with 2—again prime. So 2,339 is a right-truncatable prime. There are 83 of these in total, with the highest being 73,939,133.

There are considerably more left-truncatable primes—4,260 in total—with the highest being 357,686,312,646,216,567,629,137 (check it for yourself).

There are also 15 truncatable primes that fit into both categories—that is, it doesn't matter if you chop from the front or the back, you still get prime numbers. Sometimes called two-side primes, the highest is 739,397. Chopping from the front gives you 39,397, 9,397, 397, 97, and 7 (all prime) and chopping from the back gives you 73,939, 7393, 739, 73, 7 (again all prime).

10^{100}

A googol

The word Google is synonymous with modern life—one of the world's most famous companies and a verb for searching the Internet for information. And its name was inspired by mathematics. A googol is 1 followed by 100 zeroes and it takes its name from the imagination of a nine-year-old boy. In 1920, American mathematician Edward Kasner was talking to his nephew—Milton Sirotta—when the child came up with the name. Kasner would go on to write the book *Mathematics and the Imagination* in 1940, which brought the term into common use.

When Larry Page and Sergey Brin were looking for a name for their new Internet search engine, they needed something better than its working title of BackRub. In casting around for an alternative, they turned to the word googol, because it signified a huge amount, like the vast amounts of data their search engine was capable of indexing. They did, however, accidentally misspell it. It is said that one of their colleagues at Stanford University, Sean Anderson, mistyped it when searching to see if google.com was already in use. The name stuck.

We are now moving into the territory of incredibly big numbers, and analogies for their size begin to take on astronomical proportions. For example, if you started counting from 1 all the way up to a googol, it would take you considerably longer than the current age of the universe.

$$2^{21,701} - 1$$

The 25th Mersenne prime

Finding primes isn't only the domain of high-flying professors at prestigious academic institutions. On November 14, 1978, news broke that two 18-year-old American high school students had discovered the 25th Mersenne prime—at the time the highest one known. Their discovery of this 6,533-digit number broke the record for the youngest discoverer of a Mersenne prime, made the TV news throughout the United States, and even found its way onto the front page of *The New York Times*.

Laura Nickel and Landon Curt Noll had researched Mersenne primes and gleaned information from the math department at California State University. Then they used a computer there to run a program to search for Mersenne primes when it wasn't busy with some other task. Their program ran for 440 hours in total. It then took three years to prove the number they had found was indeed prime.

Nickel and Noll ceased working together after their discovery, but Noll continued to look for primes. He went on to find the 26th Mersenne prime, which is $2^{23,209} - 1$ (a number with 13,395 digits), using the same technique. Noll went on to work for Silicon Graphics, a company that would help set future prime records via their involvement with the Great Internet Mersenne Prime Search (GIMPS; see opposite page).

▲ Landon Curt Noll (b. 1960) codiscovered what was then the highest prime number ever found when he was just 18 years old.

$2^{74,207,281} -1$

The largest prime number currently known

As of early 2016, the largest prime number known to mathematics is $2^{74,207,281} -1$. It contains a staggering 22,338,618 digits. If you were to read every one of its digits, at the rate of one digit per second, it would take you almost nine months of continuous reading to reach the end of the number.

The 49th Mersenne prime (see opposite page), it was discovered on September 17, 2015, by Dr. Curtis Cooper of the University of Central Missouri, using software installed on his computer as part of the Great Internet Mersenne Prime Search (GIMPS). At the time, the system, which harnesses spare power from dormant computers, was using more than 360,000 CPUs to perform 150 trillion calculations per second. It has been ranked in the top 500 most powerful computer systems in the world. If your computer is the one to find a new prime, then you're in line for a cash reward of up to $50,000. The Electronic Frontier Foundation has also put up $250,000 for any group or individual who can find a billion-digit prime number.

GIMPS began in 1996, when it was founded by the American computer scientist George Woltman, and it has since found more than a dozen Mersenne primes, many of which were the highest at the time they were unearthed. The system uses the Lucas–Lehmer test, partly devised by Édouard Lucas (see page 91), to determine whether or not a number is prime.

$10^{10^{10^{34}}}$

Skewes' number

By now you should have realized that mathematicians are obsessed with prime numbers, ways of generating them, and the patterns they create. So it should be no surprise that the primes are involved in a number once described by G. H. Hardy (see page 116) as "the largest number which has ever served any definite purpose in mathematics"—Skewes' number.

To see the relevance of Skewes' number, we must first look at the distribution of prime numbers. Mathematicians have a notation for showing how many prime numbers exist that are equal to or lower than some other number. If it were the number of primes equal to or lower than 100 (which is 25), they would write $\pi(100) = 25$. It's worth noting that in this instance π is just a symbol and has nothing to do with circles.

The trouble is there's no mathematical function, $f(x)$, that gives exactly the right answer to $\pi(x)$ when various values of x are plugged in. Carl Friedrich Gauss (see page 70) did come up with a function that was a good approximation to it. Known as $\mathrm{li}(x)$, it results from an integration (see page 110) involving the natural logarithm (see page 104). The higher the value of x, the better $\mathrm{li}(x)$ approximates $\pi(x)$. However, it was long thought this would always be an overapproximation, that $\mathrm{li}(x)$ would always give an answer ever so slightly higher than $\pi(x)$. Said another way, if you plotted both functions on a graph, the line representing $\mathrm{li}(x)$ would always be slightly higher and the two lines would never cross.

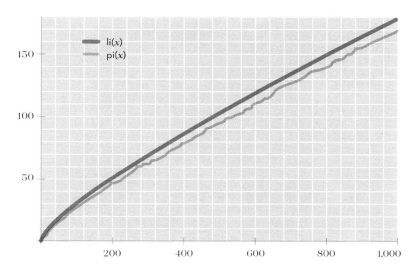

It was thought that the function li(x) would always over-approximate pi(x), but Stanley Skewes found the point at which the two lines eventually cross.

Then, in 1914, British mathematician John Littlewood showed the two lines must cross at some point. In fact, he showed they must cross an infinite amount of times. However, he wasn't able to give the first value of x at which they crossed. That fell to his student, South African mathematician Stanley Skewes, who calculated it in 1933. The only condition is that the Riemann hypothesis is true (see page 153).

His answer was that it had to be less than $e^{e^{e^{79}}}$ where e is Euler's number (see page 22). Written in base-10, this is a staggering $10^{10^{10^{34}}}$—a number so large that even if every single atom in the universe were converted into ink, there still wouldn't be enough material to write the number out long hand. In fact, there wouldn't be enough atoms in a googol copies of our universe, or a googol googol, or even a googol googol googol. You would need to write the word googol out 10^{31} times just to get the number of universes that would give you enough atoms to pen Skewes' number in full.

Later, in 1955, Skewes calculated the value this upper bound would take if the Riemann hypothesis turned out not to be true. In this case, it would be $e^{e^{e^{e^{7.705}}}}$ or $10^{10^{10^{964}}}$. Suffice to say that's even bigger, but not as big as our next number.

(Based on 3↑↑↑↑3)

Graham's number

We now encounter a number once recognized by the Guinness Book of World Records as the world's biggest. So big, in fact, that it is the only number in this book that can't be neatly written down in the title! It was formulated by American mathematician Ron Graham in the 1970s when looking at an area of combinatorics called Ramsey theory.

Imagine a square with four vertices and six lines joining them. You also have only two colors—red and blue—with which to draw the lines. Is it possible to draw them in such a way that all the lines are not the same color? The answer is pretty trivial—of course it is, just do some lines red and some blue. Graham was interested in whether a monochrome copy of this shape—let's nickname it the "crossbox"—could continue to be avoided in higher dimensions.

Take the cube, which has eight vertices and 28 lines connecting them. Can you draw these lines with only red and blue in such a way that a monochrome crossbox never appears as part of the cube? The answer is yes. You can keep upping the dimensions, too, creating what mathematicians call a "hypercube." A monochrome crossbox can always be avoided in hypercubes up to 12 dimensions. For a 13-dimensional hypercube, the jury is still out.

Graham calculated the maximum number of dimensions required to guarantee that incorporating

▼ American mathematician Ron Graham (b. 1935) came up with his really big number when looking at an area of mathematics that is called Ramsey theory.

a monochrome crossbox is unavoidable. That's Graham's number. Yet it is so large that a whole new form of notation is required to write it —"up-arrow notation," devised by American Donald Knuth in 1976. Written in this way, the basis of Graham's number is: $3 \uparrow\uparrow\uparrow\uparrow 3$.

Let's start smaller.

$3 \uparrow 3$ is simply 3^3 or 27.

$3 \uparrow\uparrow 3$ is $3\uparrow (3\uparrow 3)$, which is then $3^{(3\uparrow 3)} = 3^{27} = 7{,}625{,}597{,}484{,}987$.

Now things start getting big. Really big. $3 \uparrow\uparrow\uparrow 3 = 3 \uparrow\uparrow (3 \uparrow\uparrow 3) = 3^{7,625,597,484,987}$. The answer to this contains 3.6 trillion digits—significantly more than the highest known prime number (see page 163). Reading every single one of its digits at the rate of one per second, without ever stopping, would take you longer than 100,000 years. Suffice to say, then, that $3 \uparrow\uparrow\uparrow\uparrow 3$ is truly beyond human contemplation. And yet that's not even Graham's number.

What $3 \uparrow\uparrow\uparrow\uparrow 3$ is actually telling you is the number of arrows to put between the two 3s to then begin a process to obtain Graham's number! The result of two 3s with $3 \uparrow\uparrow\uparrow\uparrow 3$ arrows between them is called g_1. You then obtain g_2 by putting a number of arrows equal to g_1 between two 3s. Next, g_3 is calculated by putting a number of arrows equal to g_2 between two 3s. You keep on going for 64 steps to reach g_{64}. This, finally, is Graham's number. Two 3s separated by a g_{63} number of up arrows.

Infinity

No book on mathematics would be complete without mention of infinity. Yet, strictly speaking, it isn't actually a number. Instead, it is the notion of endlessness. Nevertheless, it is a highly important concept in mathematics. It is represented by the symbol ∞, which is known as the "lemniscate" and was introduced by the English mathematician John Wallis in the mid-seventeenth century. However, the idea that something can go on and on forever dates back more than two thousand years before Wallis to ancient Greek and Indian mathematicians.

It is easy to see where the notion of infinity comes from. If you start counting upward, you'll quickly notice that you can keep adding 1 and find another number in the list. You can go on and on without end.

Yet there's a fact about infinity that surprises people when they first hear about it: you can have different sizes of infinity. This idea was shown to be true by German mathematician Georg Cantor in 1891, using an area of mathematics called set theory.

Unusual accommodation

David Hilbert (see page 54) came up with a famous illustration of just how counterintuitive the different sizes of infinity can be. It's called Hilbert's Hotel. Imagine a completely booked hotel that has an infinite number of rooms. A new guest then turns up looking for accommodation. Can she stay the night? In a conventional hotel with a finite number of rooms, the answer would clearly be no. But

Georg Cantor (1845–1918)

Best known for his work on set theory, Georg Ferdinand Ludwig Philipp Cantor was born in Russia but moved to Germany when he was 11 years old. The eldest of six children, he would later go on to have six children himself with his wife, Vally Guttmann.

During a vacation in Switzerland, Cantor met and became firm friends with fellow German mathematician Richard Dedekind. Almost 14 years his senior, Dedekind would prove a rich source of inspiration for Cantor.

His ideas on set theory are now greatly celebrated, but at the time they were so abstract and counterintuitive that many of his contemporaries found them hard to believe. Henri Poincaré, of Poincaré conjecture fame (see page 153), referred to his ideas as a "grave disease."

Cantor was known to experience bouts of depression, having had his first recorded episode in 1884. He retired in 1913 and died in a sanatorium on January 6, 1918.

with Hilbert's infinite hotel, all the manager has to do is to create space by shifting the person currently in room 1 into room 2 and then the person in room 2 to room 3, etc. Because the hotel is endless, everyone can stay and the new guest can move into room 1.

What if an infinite number of people turn up looking for lodging? Easy. Just move all the current guests into the room that is double the number of their current room (so 1 to 2, 2 to 4, 3 to 6, etc). At a stroke, all the odd-numbered rooms are vacant ready for the new guests.

Further reading

Books

Bellos, Alex. *Alex Through the Looking Glass: How Life Reflects Numbers, and Numbers Reflect Life.* Bloomsbury Paperbacks, 2015.

Bellos, Alex. *Alex's Adventures in Numberland.* Bloomsbury Paperbacks, 2011.

Birch, Hayley, Mun-Keat Looi, and Colin Stuart. *The Big Questions in Science: The Quest to Solve the Great Unknowns.* Andre Deutsch, 2013.

Brown, Richard. *30-Second Maths: The 50 Most Mind-Expanding Theories in Mathematics, Each Explained in Half a Minute.* Icon Books, 2012.

Cheng, Eugenia. *Cakes, Custard and Category Theory: Easy Recipes for Understanding Complex Maths.* Profile Books, 2015.

Clegg, Brian. *Brief History of Infinity: The Quest to Think the Unthinkable.* Robinson, 2003.

Devlin, Keith. *The Millennium Problems: The Seven Greatest Unsolved Mathematical Puzzles of Our Time.* Basic Books, 2003.

du Sautoy, Marcus. *The Music of the Primes: Why an Unsolved Problem in Mathematics Matters.* Harper Perennial, 2004.

Eastaway, Rob, and John Haigh. *Beating the Odds: The Hidden Mathematics of Sport.* Robson Books, 2007.

Eastaway, Rob, and Jeremy Wyndham. *Why Do Buses Come in Threes: The Hidden Mathematics of Everyday Life.* Robson Books, 2003.

Ellenburg, Jordan. *How Not to be Wrong: The Hidden Maths of Everyday Life.* Penguin, 2015.

Euclid. *Euclid's Elements.* Green Lion Press, 2002.

Glendinning, Paul. *Maths in Minutes: 200 Keys Concepts Explained in an Instant.* Quercus, 2012.

Mlodinow, Leonard. *Euclid's Window: The Story of Geometry from Parallel Lines to Hyperspace.* Penguin, 2003.

Parker, Matt. *Things to Make and Do in the Fourth Dimension.* Penguin, 2015.

Seife, Charles. *Zero: The Biography of a Dangerous Idea.* Souvenir Press, 2000.

Singh, Simon. *Fermat's Last Theorem: The Story of a Riddle that Confounded the World's Greatest Minds for 358 Years.* Fourth Estate, 2002.

Singh, Simon. *The Simpsons and Their Mathematical Secrets.* Bloomsbury Paperbacks, 2014.

Stewart, Ian. *Seventeen Equations that Changed the World.* Profile Books, 2013.

Strogatz, Steven. *The Joy of X: A Guided Tour of Mathematics from One to Infinity.* Atlantic Books, 2013.

Tammet, Daniel. *Thinking in Numbers: How Maths Illuminates Our Lives.* Hodder Paperbacks, 2013.

Wells, David. *The Penguin Dictionary of Curious and Interesting Numbers.* Penguin, 1997.

Useful websites

Alex Bellos's Puzzles
www.theguardian.com/profile/alexbellos

American Mathematical Society www.ams.org

Ars Mathematica www.arsmathematica.net

Clay Mathematics Institute www.claymath.org

Famous mathematicians
www.famous-mathematicians.com

Institute of Mathematics and its Applications
www.ima.org.uk

International Mathematical Union www.mathunion.org

MacTutor History of Mathematics archive
www-history.mcs.st-and.ac.uk

Math Central mathcentral.uregina.ca

Math TV www.mathtv.com

Maths Careers www.mathscareers.org.uk

Mathscasts www.sites.google.com/mathscasts

Mathway www.mathway.com

NRich www.nrich.maths.org

Numberphile www.numberphile.com

Plus plus.maths.org

TED www.ted.com/topics/math

The Abel Prize www.abelprize.no

The European Mathematical Society
www.euro-math-soc.eu

The Fields Medal
www.mathunion.org/general/prizes/fields

The London Mathematical Society www.lms.ac.uk

The Operational Research Society
www.theorsociety.com

The Royal Statistical Society www.rss.org.uk

What's special about this number?
www.stetson.edu/~efriedma/numbers.html

Wolfram Alpha www.wolframalpha.com

Periodicals

Note: Almost all math periodicals are from membership organizations rather than freely available to members of the public.

Index

174

Picture credits